MARGINS OF THE SEA

MARGINS OF
THE SEA

by

MAURICE BURTON

HARPER & BROTHERS, PUBLISHERS
NEW YORK

CONTENTS

48183

LIST OF ILLUSTRATIONS

LIST OF ILLUSTRATIONS

LIST OF ILLUSTRATIONS

CHAPTER ONE

ROUGH SEAS ON SHORE

IF a large chunk of the Earth had not been thrown off, as we are assured it was, to continue spinning round our globe as the satellite we call the Moon, the human race might never have been born. This is perhaps an extravagant assertion, but it has its germ of truth, and it fulfils its purpose of pin-pointing the seashore as one of the major influences in the evolution of the plants and animals living to-day on land. The seashore is a no-man's-land between the oceans and the land masses, where the rise and fall of the tides make conditions more rigorous than in the deep waters or on dry land. It could, in effect, be regarded as a testing ground for amphibious living, and although it is highly probable that the first animals to emerge on to dry land permanently did so from the fresh-waters, they served their apprenticeship in that narrow strip bordering the continents, the turncoat margin which ceaselessly and for ever owes allegiance first to the dry land, then to the sea.

It would, however, be wrong, to give all the credit to the moon, or to put all the blame on it, for the exacting conditions obtaining in the margins of the sea. It merely plays the chief part in causing the tide to rise and fall. By so doing it sets the stage for others forces to play, for the waves to beat on it, the summer heat to dry it, the winter cold to freeze it, so that nothing can live on it that does not possess the means of combating or riding out the incessant change from one extreme to another. This, then, is my thesis, that the seashore is more than a pleasant place for a summer holiday, it is one of the more important cradles of evolution, and, so far as the succession of life on land is concerned, the most important.

This is not the first time the theory has been postulated, though perhaps not in these precise terms, although I have no doubt that it has presented itself as a passing thought to many. It may even be that the angels have feared to put into print what I am now putting into permanent form, because of the difficulty of upholding, let alone proving it. Even to uphold it adequately would require a detailed and broad knowledge of zoology and botany as a whole—a grasp of marine biology alone would not be sufficient—as well as a fair understanding of the geological history of at least a moderate number of living forms. Some knowledge of physical oceanography, too, would be required to do the subject justice.

It is not my purpose, therefore, to seek to defend my theory to the full against all comers. Rather, it is an idea which commends itself to me, which seems on reflection to be a potentially fruitful source of study, and one which, as a broad generalisation, is likely to be true. The way of the pioneer is hard, but at least when he has laboriously felled the trees to break up the ground they occupied, he will have done one thing, if no more: he will have opened up another view. I am further comforted by the thought that so often, in speaking to lay audiences or leading a discussion, it is not so much the information imparted as the argument provoked that gives the most enjoyment. Furthermore, once interest has been aroused, the most enjoyable sessions have been those in which the discussions have wandered to any item of interest that may crop up or commend itself. It is in such a discursive mood that I shall follow up my theme, and, while assuming that it was in the littoral that the primary requirements for life on land were set in train, examine the biological principles needing to be satisfied to make successful the emergence on to dry land.

We are constantly informed that the sea offers a stable environment as compared with that on land. The grounds for this statement are the numerous data on temperature and salinity, the behaviour of currents and the other physical factors laboriously gathered by research ships and painstakingly analysed in the laboratory and the study. From the results so obtained we know that conditions in the sea are more equable than on land. In a hot desert,— for there are also cold deserts, such as the Gobi desert—the days are blisteringly hot, the nights cold; there is little water and little vegetation and the fight against desiccation and starvation are never-ending. No parallel set of conditions is to be found in the sea. Even in the more temperate regions, night and day, the changing seasons, the air-currents, the rains and other meteorological events, bring a diversity of conditions which, likewise, are probably unparalleled in the sea. Even so, I feel that the generalisation, that the sea offers a stable environment, cannot be accepted as a complete statement of the truth.

It has long been observed that every now and then, occurring more especially, but not solely, in certain parts of the world, the shore is littered with thousands of carcases. I have several photographs, for instance, of the harbours on the Chile coast choked with the dead and rotting carcases of squid. I have seen other photographs of the coast of south-west Africa almost literally covered with dead fish. These mass-deaths as they were called, and which were the source of some mystification and speculation for a long time, are now fairly certainly explained by up-wellings of cold water, from Humboldt's Current sweeping up the Pacific coast of South America, and from the Benguela Current running in a similar manner up the Atlantic coast of Africa.

McNeill and Livingstone, writing in the *Australian Museum Magazine* in 1926, tell how since 1856 Rivers of Blood, Red Slime or Red Tide has occurred every year, in smaller or larger quantities. When in large quantities, in plague form, that is, the various explanations offered were that the phenomenon was the result of large quantities of earthy matter in the sea or waste products, or pollution from the paper mills or sugar works, or from blood and offal from the abattoirs. None of these explanations proved correct, but they are given here because they illustrate vividly the intensity of the phenomenon. The best explanation offered was that the phenomenon was comparable to the appearance of small red microscopic plants which have given the Red Sea its name. These Red Tides of Sydney Harbour, which killed off fish, oysters, mussels and other marine populations proved also to be due to plagues of microscopic plants or plant-like organisms.

From the opposite end of the world, off California, a similar event was chronicled in 1946, where hundreds of lobsters came up on to the beach at Santa Monica, to be had for the asking. At the same time, offshore, there was a plague of Peridinians, microscopic organisms, red in colour, belonging to the class which neither zoologist nor botanist will own, and therefore labelled plant-animals. The experts came to the conclusion that these had denuded the water of oxygen "and other accessory chemicals", and that the lobsters had migrated out of the water to obtain oxygen from the air. Can it be that some such event has contributed to an emergence from the sea, to be followed by a permanent residence?

A somewhat different event occurred on the southern coast of the U.S.A. Gunter, writing in the *American Midland Naturalist* for 1942, tells of a sudden mortality of marine organisms in July, 1939, in Offat's Bayou, a blind inlet of water opening into Galveston Bay. Fish, shrimps, crabs and oysters died off, and the common blue crab was reported to leave the water and crawl ashore. The mortality was said to be occasioned by the "boils", areas of turbulent water up to 30 feet diameter, red and black in colour and boiling furiously with escaping gas. Foul odours accompanied the boils, which could have been due to the accumulation of dead organic matter in the Bayou (it was 30 feet deep at the inner end, with a bar across the mouth, and an average depth of some 12 feet). Even the paint on the boats went black.

Ordinary tides in the Bayou are 1 to $1\frac{1}{2}$ feet deep, and in 1940, when a hurricane swept across the Gulf of Mexico, bringing tides 3 to 4 feet deep to scour the Bayou, no boils occurred. In December 1940, however, rains of cloudburst proportions in Galveston Bay caused a big drop in the salinity of the sea, and fish took shelter in Offat's Bayou, where, Gunter reports, rod-and-line fishermen lined the banks every day for three weeks. The boils may be due to silting up of the channel, possibly aggravated by the accumulation of human waste going into the sea, but the situation does represent a local phenomenon which could occur under similar natural conditions elsewhere, especially near the mouths of sluggish rivers.

Anyone visiting the Whitsunday Group, prior to 1918, would have seen on the shore masses of beautiful corals and sponges of all colours, crowding the rocks together with other marine organisms. The Australian, Rainford, tells how when he visited the Group in 1924 he found complete desolation. The corals were blackened with decay, clams empty and gaping and animal life gone except for the sea-mosses which with seaweed grew everywhere on the reef. The damage could hardly have been due to a severe lowering of the temperature of the sea, which was one suggestion made, or it would in all likelihood have affected everything else. There was no alteration in the level of the land or of the reef, according to the gauges, nor could contamination with silt be the cause, or there would have been similar disturbance on the inner fringe of the Barrier Reef. The most likely cause seems to have been a severe cyclone which struck the coast of Northern

Queensland. In five days there was a rainfall of 26 inches. So much water came down from the rivers that a steamer eight miles off shore drew freshwater in a bucket let down over the side. This alone may have had little effect except that the rainfall coincided with the period of the deepest low tides. This, in turn, would mean that all animals on the beach would be exposed for two hours to freshwater in the surface layers. Certainly, crabs and worms were found dead in the sand, which tends to support the hypothesis.

The events described here are but a few from a large number recorded, and serve merely as samples of the hazards of life on the shore and in the shallow waters. Some are local, some are widespread; some are seasonal, some cyclic, some entirely sporadic. Some can be compared with disasters on land, of which we have often more complete data, where cataclysmic events have wiped out populations except for a few survivors that sought refuge in new lands. Has, then, the cataclysm been one of the major factors in organic evolution, and especially in the invasion of the land?

On the other hand, some of the events can be compared to the plagues of land animals. As one writer has pointed out: if one pair of rabbits were taken to New Zealand, where there are no natural enemies, their progeny would, in three years, number nine million, even if half of each generation perished. This striking but familiar example—the writer was Elizabeth C. Pope, an Australian—drives home how the variation in favourable and unfavourable factors can give rises and falls in populations. Where there is a concatenation of circumstances favourable to one species, the soaring population can react most unfavourably on other species. This is too wide a subject to be dealt with at this point. Its mention here is merely to recall that the disbalance of populations is one more adverse circumstance to be borne in mind in the course of our discussion.

Returning to the rigours of the inter-tidal zone, we can say that in addition to catastrophic events and plagues, of whatever kind, cyclic or sporadic, there is the continual pounding of the waves. My earliest lesson in this, one which many people must have experienced in more striking form, took place many years ago, when I had the fool-hardiness to bathe in a rough sea off the coast of Suffolk. It was easy going as long as I was out of my depth, for I

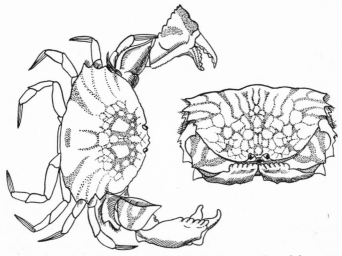

This South American crab lives exposed to the battering of the waves. With its legs drawn in it can be rolled without injury.

simply rode the swell. The trouble began when I came in to land. Almost as soon as my feet touched the shingle I was picked up and thrown against a groyne. The waves receded and I started to scramble to my feet to run up the beach, out of reach of the waves, but almost immediately another wave came in, picked me up and threw me once more against the groyne. Three times this happened before I could scramble clear. By the mercy of Providence, it so happened each time that I hit the timbers of the groyne with the muscular part of my back and sustained nothing more than a severe fright, together with bruises and minor cuts from the barnacles encrusting the groyne. I had received the first lesson I can clearly remember in marine biology, although I was not to realise this for many years.

Had I been a seal, that would not have happened, because not only is a seal specially adapted to life in the sea, but it is accustomed from birth to meet and deal with this kind of situation. Of course, seals are sometimes dashed to their death on the rocks in heavy seas, mainly while still young. Those that avoid such an untimely end are guided by instinct or learn by experience either to avoid such situations or to cope with them. Those that are killed are mainly the pups, and especially those less muscularly strong than their fellows, with less acute senses, less intelligence, or in some other way are less good at avoiding or dealing with these adverse circumstances. This is, of course, largely guesswork, but then so much of what we call Science is guesswork. We may weigh, measure or carry out precise tests of various kinds, but all, or most, of the important conclusions are guesswork; or, to be more exact, intuitive deductions against a background of more precise knowledge.

I would like to say more about seals, but let me finish with the lessons I learned in that rough encounter with the water's edge. Or, perhaps I should say, the lessons I then learned and have since realised. First that I was not specially adapted to life in the sea. Moreover, I did not bathe often enough to become adapted, or accustomed, to a life in the water. In other words, things are born to a special environment, or mode of life, and must keep to it or perish, and yet by a paradox, this same environment weeds out the weaklings. There is, in other words, a natural selection. But above all I had had my first lesson in the rigours of the margins of the sea.

It would be a mistake to suppose that it is only cataclysms and storms that comprise these rigours. Many are so subtle as to have eluded the most delicate and searching investigation. These are the result of small changes in temperature, in salinity, and so on. There are also those, comparable with the poundings of the storms, which go on incessantly even in calm weather. The next pointed lesson I received came from this cause.

It was a few years ago, when I was making an ecological survey of a piece of rocky coast in Torbay. My interest was mainly in sponges, although I was prepared to take note of anything that offered. There was on this piece of shore a pool, at about mid-tide level. It was a beautifully rounded saucer in the rock, a foot deep at the most, and some ten feet diameter, with an island in the centre: almost an ornamental pond. The edges of the saucer and the sides of the island, were coated with a growth of low tough weed and corallines. What struck me most was that there was little else living in it besides. Yet the conditions seemed ideal: it should have been one of those beautiful rock-pool sea-gardens one reads about. Puzzling over this, I decided to make a complete investigation. My first idea was that the pool probably heated up too much in sunny weather. We were then enjoying a mild heat wave, so I took a series of temperature readings during the ebb and flow of the tide. There was nothing unusual in them. The pool did heat up a little between tides but not more so than others containing a profusion of animals. Briefly, after trying every possible source of explanation, I gave up attempts to solve the problem.

I did not forsake the pool, however, for it seemed ideal for some transplanting experiments I wished to make, on sponges. This involved detaching specimens from elsewhere, fastening them to flat stones with copper wire, and planting them down where they could be readily observed. A half-dozen were put down. The next day none could be found, although the flat stones were there, some still bearing the copper wire. Then I realised what should have been obvious in the first place, that the pebbles lying so innocently on the bottom of the pool, in the quiet period when the tide was out, were lifted by the incoming tide and swirled round, converting the quiet pool into a seething cauldron. This episode gave me a clue to another puzzle about a mile away in the bay. There, at the foot of the cliffs was a flat table of rock, running out to sea for nearly a quarter of a mile at the best low tides. I had searched its surface unsuccessfully for any signs of life. There was none, except in occasional pockets in the rock and even there only a few meagre patches of barnacles were found. At low tide, the surface of the table was covered with a thin film of mud, but at the turn of the tide, the water raced across this almost horizontal ledge, seething and foaming, whipping up the mud and scouring every part of the exposed surface with its fine particles.

The effects of swirl and scour were brought out more markedly, by a series of contrasts. This was found in a group of massive rocks in another part of Torbay. Two large towering piles of rock stood side by side, with a sandy cove between. There were caves, gullies, inlets and all the variations of these. On a fine calm day, one could stand on a pinnacle of rock, look down on the sea around and note the lack of uniformity in the water. Even in that small area, about a quarter of a mile each way, at slack water low-tide, there were patches of dead still water and areas of slight turbulence. As the water rose it was easy to see the correspondence between the patches of still water and the areas on the rocks of greatest profusion of weed, sea-mosses, sponges, anemones and the rest. Where there were patches of turbulent water, or even of still water in certain instances, the surfaces of the rocks were smooth and devoid of life. In stormy weather there was no differentiation between still and turbulent patches and the rising tide beat and foamed in cave and gully, through and over the rocks, over bare surfaces and over those coated with a multitude of living organisms.

It was fairly apparent that apart from the scouring effect of pebbles, sand and mud, turbulence on its own was mainly effective in sweeping away newly-settled larvae. Given tolerably calm seas at the breeding season, therefore, for the settlement of larvae and during the early stages of growth, the maturing organisms could resist the battering of the waves, the sedentary organisms by tenacity and resilience, the free-living animals by taking shelter.

The effects of swirl and scour and wave action generally can be readily appreciated by all who have seen the breakers hurling themselves up the face of vertical cliffs in a storm, or watched the walls of water rise all along the edge of the promenade of a sea-side resort, hurling pebbles, seaweed and jetsam across its paved surface. Even the long breakers across a sandy beach in fine weather will churn the sand up with relentless force, while storm breakers over a rocky coast, churning the pebbles and sucking them back with each receding wave contain a menace apparent to eye and ear alike.

Here then is the no-man's-land between the comparative stability of the deep waters, on the one hand, and of the land, on the other hand, which must be crossed in any transition from a marine life to a terrestrial existence, whether the final step was taken across the drift-line on the coast or by way ultimately of the rivers. It is like the main hurdle in a steeplechase. We see the riders mounted on their horses line up, the signal is given and the race begins. Some horses go into the lead, others drop behind, but all are fairly on a level at first. It is the high fence ahead, the real testing point, that sorts them out. Some horses refuse the jump and are seen on the wrong side of the fence, their riders still endeavouring to coax them over. Others throw their riders and canter back towards the starting point. Some try the jump and come to grief. Others clear it and throw their riders, to canter aimlessly on the right side of the fence. The few clear the obstacle successfully, their riders still up and straggle out, making for the winning post.

The picture of the steeplechase cannot be exactly applied to the animal kingdom, but it helps in a broad way to appreciate how the various groups of animals, starting from the shallow waters offshore, have fared and the varying success they have achieved.

The two big groups of animals, as usually understood, are the invertebrates and the vertebrates. The latter comprises five classes, the mammals, birds, reptiles, amphibia and fishes, together with the less well-known Protochordata, important as representing the earlier stages of the evolution of the vertebrates. These are dealt with more fully in Chapter Fourteen. They are important, too, in our present story and a vital link in the evidence necessary to upholding my particular theory. The invertebrates include a dozen or so groups which are used arbitrarily here for the sake of convenience, although they do not necessarily conform to strict zoological classification. This enables us to ignore a number of forms, little known even to the general zoologist and sufficiently off the beaten track to contribute nothing to our story. The analysis of the distribution to-day of these various groups, in the sea, the fresh waters and on land, is given in the table facing this page. The table starts with the simplest organisms and proceeds upwards in an order of increasingly complex organisations to the mammals, which include man.

We can ignore the Protozoa, the unicellular animals, because they have made their way on to the land largely as parasites in the bodies of the truly terrestrial animals. Then we see that most of the invertebrates are marine, with slight penetrations into the freshwaters, but that with increasing complexity of bodily structure there is a greater tendency to colonise both the freshwaters and the land. In insects and spiders, the highest of the invertebrates, there

	SEA	FRESH WATER	LAND
MAMMALS			
BIRDS			
REPTILES			
AMPHIBIA			
FISHES			
PROTOCHORDATES			
SPIDERS			
INSECTS			
CRUSTACEA			
MOLLUSCS			
BRACHIOPODS (LAMP SHELLS)			
ECHINODERMS (STARFISH, SEA URCHINS)			
WORMS			
COELENTERATES (HYDROIDS, JELLYFISH, SEA ANEMONES, CORALS)			
SPONGES			
PROTOZOA			

Table showing main divisions of animal kingdom, and the extent to which they inhabit sea, freshwater or land. (Darker cross-hatching indicates a secondary return to freshwater or sea.)

are a handful of species that have returned secondarily to
the sea (represented by the stippled sections) or the freshwaters, while the vast majority of species remain truly
terrestrial. As to insects, there are so many species that
pass the early stages of the life-history in freshwater, that
the picture is apt to be confused. In the vertebrates, on the
other hand, the progression into freshwater and on to land
is so clearly evident in the table that no further explanation
is necessary.

If those of us interested in the biology of the seashore
stopped to analyse why we find its study attractive, we
should almost certainly arrive at the following conclusions. First, there is the intrinsic interest of a part of the
earth's surface which is unlike, for most of us, the world
of our normal daily life. Then there is the sheer aesthetic
enjoyment of the colours and form of so many of its
inhabitants. Apart from these, the shore is the meeting
place of terrestrial as well as marine animals and plants,
a no-man's land I have already called it, where terrestrial
creatures assemble, or venture down, and where sea
creatures come in, either to spawn or to seek prey, or
are in permanent residence. The seashore, therefore, more
than the land, is the place where anything can happen
and the most surprising things be found. Further, it gives
the opportunity of studying in detail the daily lives and
habits of creatures comparable to those living in deeper
waters where direct observation is more or less impossible. So the information we gather on the shore can
be used directly or by comparison to build up our picture
of what goes on in the inaccessible depths. Above all, we
see in concentrated form, and in miniature, the struggle
for existence and the evolution of special habits or
structures to overcome the environmental difficulties.
Nowhere else in the world is there such a variety of
habitats in so small an area, or where the conditions vary
so much from hour to hour, day to day, season to season,

and from one year to another. It is a microcosm of evolution, and to a limited extent only can the steeplechase analogy be usefully applied to the shore itself, for its inhabitants are not just distributed in a haphazard manner, but occur for the most part in zones.

It happened, a few years ago, when making the survey in Torbay, that the subject of zoning was impressed vividly on my memory. My main interest as I have said, was to study the sponges. One of the leading experts in the study of these animals was Dr H. J. Carter. In one of his numerous writings on the subject he made the remark that sponges can be found growing almost up to high-tide mark. This remark has been repeated many times since, in standard works on the subject, and there was no reason to doubt it. Since time was valuable, and it was necessary to cram as much work as possible into a minimum period, I made my way to the shore, some distance away from where I was lodging, in time to catch the tide at the moment it turned. In that way I should be able to follow the tide down, making observations all the way.

This particular piece of beach I had chosen for my purpose was somewhat out-of-the-way, approachable by a steep climb. To cut the story short, it transpired that not until the ebbing tide had reached mid-tide level did it uncover the particular beasts I had come to study. This meant a three-hour wait, with nothing to read, nothing to do, and only hard rock to sit upon. If anyone wishes for an idea of eternity let him sit for three hours watching the tide go out, for it waits for no man, nor does it hurry itself for anyone. But it was a valuable lesson, for I found that sponges are beautifully zoned, which was an entirely new discovery. Thus, almost precisely from mid-tide level down to the highest low-water of the neap tides there were three kinds of sponges only: the blood-red sponge and the crumb-of-bread sponge, with occasional patches of a white-lace sponge. From highest low-water neaps to the mean low-tide level, these three could still be found but in less quantity, and the dominant form was the purse sponge. From mean low-tide level to extreme low water springs, these four tended to peter out but in their place were a score or more species.

More will be said about zoning later on, but for the moment it is sufficient to say that both the seaweeds and the shore animals are found in definite zones, more or less. Some are well-marked, some less well-marked. Sometimes the zoning is broken up by local conditions so as not to be immediately apparent, but it can always be seen, at least approximately. It is as though we have in slow motion a race up the beach on the part of species endeavouring to reach dry land—a part of our steeplechase.

CHAPTER TWO

UP AND DOWN THE BEACH

IT is one thing to base a theory on present-day conditions and it is another thing to be sure that the same
conditions held good in the past. The question must naturally arise whether inter-tidal conditions, comparable with
those we see now, did obtain at the time that the first
plants and animals were invading the land masses. It is
believed that the earth and the moon formed originally
one rotating fluid globe and that around it, under the
gravitational pull of the sun, there swept a daily tide of
molten matter. Then the moon parted company with the
earth, and it has even been suggested that the great deeps
of the Pacific Ocean represent the gap left by the moon, as
it was thrown off into space. This must have taken place at
some time between two and three thousand million years
ago.

After the moon's departure, the red-hot earth, blanketed
from the first by gases, gradually cooled; and with the
cooling came the formation of large quantities of steam
which condensed to form the first oceans and seas. The
first living matter is believed to have appeared fifteen
million years ago, but no trace of it remains except in the
rocks laid down in the last five hundred million years. The
thousand million years prior to this, the period of pre-
history of the earth, and especially of living matter on the
earth, belongs very much to the realm of surmise. This surmise rests, however, on the results of several lines of investigation, all of which lead to the same conclusions. They
may differ slightly, but the differences are remarkably
small, and of recent years investigations and calculations

based on radioactivity of the rocks have amply confirmed
the conclusions earlier reached on less precise grounds.
This thousand million years, the so called pre-Cambrian
period, does contain, however, towards its close a few
scanty remains of living things. Then, by the beginning of
the Cambrian period, suddenly, measured in geological
times, the invertebrates are much in evidence.

This long gap from the supposed inception of life on the
earth to the beginning of the fossil record is unfortunate
from the evolutionist's point-of-view, in that it denies us
vital evidence. It is also puzzling. It has been suggested
that the absence of fossils from the pre-Cambrian was because the animals were mainly soft-bodied. Yet some
traces of animal life have been found in it, including the
horny shells of early lamp-shells, traces of worms and the
imprints of jelly-fish; and nothing, surely, could be more
soft-bodied than a jelly-fish. Traces of early plants with
calcareous skeletons were also found, not so remarkably
unlike seaweeds with chalky skeletons living to-day in the
rock-pools on the shore. So it seems clear that while it is
not possible fully to account for this gap in our knowledge,
the general supposition, that animals and plants did live
then, is probably correct. Indeed, the fact that some remains were found in the pre-Cambrian puts this beyond
reasonable doubt.

During the Cambrian period, which lasted for a hundred million years, the seas slowly encroached on the land,
and all animal life was marine. The next seventy million
years of the Ordovician period saw the appearance of the
first vertebrates, heavily-armoured fish-like Ostracoderms.
And during this time there was a marked recession of the
sea, leaving large areas of dry land. In the Silurian period
that followed, there is abundant evidence of a profusion
of animal life, in reefs in shallow seas, whose massive skeletons seem designed to withstand the buffeting of rough
seas. We are justified, therefore, in assuming not only a

tidal influence from the pull of both sun and moon, but similar rigours at the seas margins such as we are familiar with to-day. In the Silurian and the Devonian periods, land plants were established, and in the latter period, which began a little over three hundred million years ago, often called the Age of Fishes, there was a rapid evolution of the aquatic vertebrates. These included the ancestors of the Coelacanth, which caused such a stir in recent years. By the end of the Devonian, the first Amphibia had come into existence.

Although it was the Amphibia which gave rise to the reptiles, birds and mammals, and finally man himself, they were not the first animals to come ashore. Woodlice, spiders, mites, millipedes and wingless insects had preceded them. It could not have been otherwise. It must have happened that the plants were the first to arrive, followed by animals that fed on them or their remains; and both paved the way, from the point of food supply, for the larger animals.

Even from this brief survey, it is clear that as far back as three hundred million years ago, the invasion of the land was well under way, and the stage was set for the later evolution of the vertebrates.

Our knowledge of the tides or of their effects on marine life during these remote periods is very fragmentary, but we may be confident that it will be pieced together in time, although, naturally, the final picture can never be as complete as that of the shore to-day. Any speculation on the part played by the littoral zone and the rise and fall of the tides in the evolution of terrestrial organisms must be largely based on the study of the present, and on the comparison we can make between the results so obtained and what the geologist can tell us.

Now, twice a day on most shores, the tide ebbs and flows, except in such places as the Mediterranean, which is practically tideless, Weymouth which has four tides a

day and Southampton with its six tides a day. Twice a
month when there is a united pull by the moon and the
sun, that is at the new and full moon, the tides are
unusually high and unusually low. This is the period of the
spring tides. When the moon and the sun are pulling at
right angles, that is at about the first and last quarters, the
tides, known as neap tides, are shallow. To recognise the
existence of spring and neap tides is sufficient for ordinary
purposes, but some people need to subdivide them further.
Among these are the marine biologists, whose charts of the
shore show lines of maximum high tide springs, maximum
low tide springs, mid-tide level (or mean tide-level),
mean low water, mean high water, minimum low water
neaps, minimum low water springs and so on. In fact, the
marine biologist to-day has made his map of the shore so
complicated with regard to tide levels that only a specialist has the patience or the need to understand them. Added
to these zones, there is also the drift line, just above the
highest spring-tide mark, where the flotsam and jetsam
accumulate. There is also a splash zone, moistened by
spray to a varying degree according to the height of the
tide and the prevailing weather. Even the splash zone has
been further subdivided.

All these have an importance for our present enquiry,
although it will be sufficient to speak here in round terms
of the springs and neaps, high and low tides, mid-tide,
drift-line and splash zone. The importance of these zones
is that they determine the kind of life inhabiting them and
produce some of the varying conditions which help to
mould the form and the habits of the life of the shore.

The plants and animals living on the shore are not distributed haphazardly. For the most part, each species
occupies a well-defined zone, which may not necessarily
conform to a recognised tidal zone. Even children are
aware of this although they have probably never even
heard the words marine biology, much less such cryptic

phrases as mean low water of spring tides. Their interest
is to take a bucket and spade on to the shore, to dig in the
sand or, much more exciting, collect in the bucket these
strange things they find under slabs of rocks, or sheltering
in the spaces between the boulders, or even sometimes
stranded high and dry on the sand as the tide goes out.
They are aware of the fact that yesterday the tide went out
a long way, so far, in fact, that when it was at its lowest ebb
the broad oarweeds made an almost continuous carpet
just under the surface of the water, gently rising and falling
as the sea lazily heaved at the edge of the beach. To tell a

Small crabs, half an inch across, that
look like water-worm pebbles or fragments
of coral rock.

child that this is the Laminarian-zone would go in one of
its ears and out of the other. But it would know that when
the tide went out this far an unfamiliar piece of beach was
uncovered and that it was one which offered more than
the usual opportunities for picking up crabs, starfish and
other things not found further up the beach. It would also
know that at such times one might even find a small
octopus or cuttle in the inch-deep water this side of the
oarweed or Laminaria, as the marine botanist calls it.

That same child would be aware a few days later that
the tide went out later in the day and that it did not go

out so far as at the beginning of the week. And that when it did not go out so far there were not so many exciting things to be found, for in the zone of the spring tides we get a fair representation of the marine life lying beyond the tidal or littoral zone of the shore. Let us now take a closer look round the shore with the eyes of a child, that is, with the eyes and mind of a layman who is unhampered by a wealth of technical terms and the need for a precision in definition. And this is sufficient, for no great erudition is needed to know that what we find on the shore will depend not only on the state of the tide but also on the type of shore we are examining. A pebble beach will be almost completely barren, except for empty shells, for the most part broken. A shingle shore is little better, and at first glance a sandy shore seems without life. A sandy shore has this advantage, however, that at low tide a little amateur sleuthing is possible.

If we walk down a sandy beach, keeping the eyes glued to the ground we shall find many tell-tale signs. Up near high-tide mark, recognisable by the fairly continuous line of dried seaweed, with its pieces of wood, candle ends, cotton waste and all the flotsam and jetsam that make up the drift-line, there will be nothing. We shall, of course, find if we dislodge the line of drift that we have disturbed the innumerable sand-hoppers, characteristic scavengers, one of many scavengers of the shore. We shall also see the occasional shapeless mass of bleached carrion, shapeless usually beyond recognition, with its temporary popula- tions of flies, belonging more properly to the land but ready to invade the shore if a meal offers, demonstrating that tidemarks and shore alike do not constitute a hard-and-fast boundary. But a few feet below the drift-line the truly marine inhabitants will start to disclose their presence. Perhaps the first we shall see will be a patch of minute tubes peeping through the sand, looking as though a number of bicycle valve tubes had been surreptitiously buried in a vertical position. They are worm-tubes, one of many different kinds found at various points on this beach. Some, also looking like rubber tubes, but larger, on being handled readily break up into seemingly horny fragments. Others are constructed of sand-grains as neatly set as the bricks in a wall, without visible means of support, crumbling readily in the fingers yet sufficiently firmly held together and having enough resilience that they can withstand the daily pounding of the surf as the tide races in on the flow.

A little below mid-tide mark, uncovered twice a day, even on the neap tides, and therefore battered twice a day, we may find a solitary boulder, half-buried in the sand, its seaward face decorated by a lump of sandy mosaic which resolves itself, on closer examination, into a tightly-packed mass of sandy tubes. It has always been a marvel to me that these particular worm-tubes, which often form sizeable reefs, can be broken so easily with the fingers yet appear to suffer so little from the regular beating of the surf. Remembering my own experience of being thrown against the groyne, I should expect such fragile tubes to suffer irreparable damage. At low-tide the inhabitant of each tube is withdrawn into its inner recesses, away from the drying effect of wind and sun. Even if we dig it out, we see no more than an ordinary-looking worm, with this difference from the earthworm, that each side of its body is decorated with a line of bristle laden lobes, and that the head bears a tangled mass of fine thread-like tentacles. It needs a little imagination to picture those tentacles extended, when the tide is full up, gracefully waving and reaching out to catch whatever may be suspended in the water, food-particles to be passed down the length of the tentacle by microscopic protoplasmic hairs to the mouth. And sand-grains also, to be passed down in the same way and, if the tube is in need of repair, or needs extending, being moistened with saliva and placed in position at the appropriate point on the tube. It may be that the surf does damage the tubes and that as often as they are damaged they are repaired. On the other hand, it may be that they do not often suffer damage, or need repair, for there is this about natural fabrications, as contrasted with the man-made buildings and machines, that they have a resiliency and a resistance to the elements which we find difficult to copy.

There are other worms than those that build tubes, and we are almost bound to see somewhere on the sandy beach the paired traces of the lugworm: to one side the heap of coiled sandy castings and within a few inches of it the saucer-like depression in the sand. Beneath we should find the U-shaped tube; within it is the lugworm, reminiscent of the more familiar earthworm. Like the earthworm it lives by passing the sand or mud it inhabits through its digestive tube, taking the contained particles for food and rejecting a mixture of indigestible quartz grains and its own excrement. Both are scavengers, cleansing agents continually at work, reducing the fragments of dead plant and animal bodies to still finer proportions for smaller beings than themselves, ultimately to the bacteria, to work upon. Thus, what was originally vegetation or solid flesh is converted into soluble chemicals to feed the plants and set the whole food cycle once more in motion.

There will be other things than worms in a sandy beach. But all will be out of sight at low tide. Many will be out of sight even after the tide has returned, merely then pushing their siphons, for feeding, breathing and excreting, a little above the level of the sand, passing water through their bodies, taking in oxygen and food-particles, and letting the same stream of water carry out the by-products of their own digestion. Many molluscs lie so hidden: the razor-shells, cockles and anything up to a hundred different kinds, of various shapes, sizes and colours. The masked crab, too, may be there, completely submerged in the sand in a vertical position, with its antennae close together, their bristles interlocking and forming a siphon for feeding and breathing as efficient as the soft fleshy siphons of the bivalves.

The masked crab is not easy to find. Usually it follows the water down the beach, coming out from its sandy retreat as the water ebbs from about it, waddling down to the water's edge and beyond to submerge once again. We

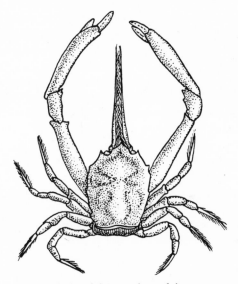

The masked-crab burrows in sand, its antennae forming a breathing tube.

may, however, see its tracks, like a double row of holes made with the fine point of a penknife blade. There will be other tracks of the same sort, for the shore crab will often run across the sand and, for no obvious reason, but presumably because it feels exposed to danger, dig its way down, submerging fairly rapidly, the last thing to disappear being the stalked eyes. Irregular lines drawn in the

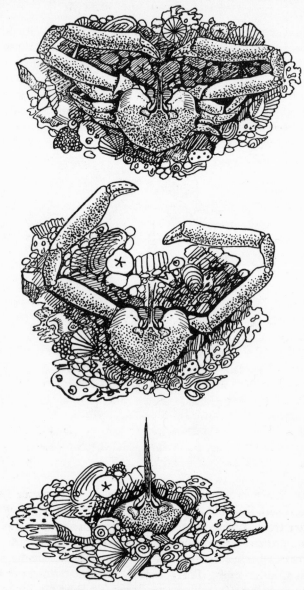

A masked-crab submerges in the sand, leaving finally
only its antennae exposed.

surface of the sand, as with the point of the finger or with a pencil point, and ending abruptly, all tell the same story, of some living thing that has retired beneath the surface for greater security or for greater opportunities for feeding. The treacherous sand is a safe retreat from its own dangers. Only those things that can take refuge in its substance can long survive the scouring as the returning waves, the surf at the water's edge, lifts the upper layers of the sand in a boiling cloud of abrasive particles. The sandy beach, then, is for those that have learned to burrow in the sand, that are equipped to feed on particles of animal flesh and the disintegrating tissues of seaweeds from more richly populated parts of the sea, or on the numberless microscopic plants and animals that abound everywhere in the surface waters of the sea.

The rocky shores give us a marked contrast. Here are the things that cling; and nothing clings more firmly than seaweed, to provide a rich pasture and a shelter from the elements and from living enemies for a much wider variety of animal life. Here, too, are the limpets, hanging on by the suction of the foot, barnacles permanently anchored by the head, sea-anemones that also hold on by suction and by the gum-like mucus given off from the base of the body, which move as freely as a limpet though less often and more erratically. The rocks give anchorage to innumerable hosts of mussels, fixed all but permanently by the byssus, the so-called beard, a cluster of brown horny threads. Each thread is fastened, like the creeper's tendrils on the walls of the house, by a terminal sucker, the mechanics of which are not easy to elucidate. Mussels are safe from the pounding of the surf, their byssus threads so tough that at least one pair of gloves was woven from them, a task more novel than profitable. A mussel may on occasion change its position, by severing the anchoring byssus thread, throwing out new threads and pulling on them, "inching it" in a manner and at a pace which is tedious by human standards. But for the mussel life is simple and time has no meaning.

Starfish, and their relatives the sea-urchins, have another method of clinging to the rock, although the principle underlying it does not differ materially from those we have already discussed. In them the skin extends into a series of suckers, or tube-feet, each of small size but maintaining a sufficient grip that a starfish suddenly and forcibly removed from a rock may leave one or more behind, still clinging to the rock surface. The combined effect of scores or hundreds of such efficient holdfasts provides an effective counter to the mighty power of turbulent water.

Rocks provide other things than surfaces to cling to; and every topographical feature of a large irregular boulder has its peculiar population. Each crack and crevice, on its top, sides or undersurfaces, whether on the seaward or the landward face, has its particular community of animals, each having different requirements of food, and each having a different toleration of light, temperature, wetness and all the other physical factors. The study of any one boulder would reveal a wide range of different groupings of animals, a large number of different species and a wide range of structural modifications, so that each animal is able to occupy a particular niche in a highly variable terrain. These range from the shore crab that takes a temporary residence under a convenient overhang, into which it retires backwards as the water recedes, to the most minute water shrimps or water fleas—the name we give is entirely optional for they are too inconspicuous and unfamiliar ever to have received a common name—living in the furthermost recesses of a crevice too narrow to admit the human fingers.

A boulder-strewn coast, plentifully covered with weed, may be compared with the jungles on land. Both offer a wide variety of habitats for innumerable animals, of all sizes and types, with abundant food; a rich population unfamiliar except to the prying eye of the naturalist, but all having some story to tell, some quota to contribute to the main theme of the evolution of life, when that story has been laboriously and painstakingly pieced together.

The populations on the rocky coast, then, differ markedly from those on the sandy shore. But in a single stretch of coast we are likely to meet a wide variety of types of shore: the rock, sand, mixed sand and rock, pebble, shingle, and near the mouths of rivers, sandy-mud or pure mud, providing an infinite variety of physical conditions, an infinite variety of habitats. There will be some animal peculiar to one or the other, some—the more specialised—that can live only in a restricted habitat. But there are some that can be looked for with success on almost any type of shore, although not necessarily in any type of situation. The ubiquitous shore-crab, for example, will be found among rocks, on the sand or mud, well up the estuaries of rivers, even in the brackish streamlets in a salt-marsh. In habit, at least, they are more generalised.

More will be said in later chapters about the zoning of the shore, and it will be sufficient at this point to draw a general picture. It is seen most obviously in the sea-weeds, but on no shore is it necessarily regular, and in many places the local conditions produce such alterations that it is difficult to recognise. At one point on the south coast of England, for example, concrete groynes run out to extreme low-water mark at intervals of about a hundred yards. Not only does the type of substratum differ between adjacent pairs of groynes, sandy in one, shingle in another, mixed sand and rock in another, and so on, but the zoning of the seaweeds has also become confused. One has green weed, the so-called sea lettuce, and practically nothing else, down to low-water neaps, while in the next bay the zoning of the weed has a text-book regularity. Allowing for these exceptions, we can nevertheless draw our typical picture, best seen on the rocky shore.

Going from the land towards high-water mark, we pass the typical land flora and fauna, which peters out in the splash-zone, best seen on the face of a cliff, where the area wetted by salt spray will contain grasses and other plants, especially such things as thrift. There also we shall find spiders in the crevices in the cliff face and at the same level sea-slaters, looking like large and grotesque woodlice, running quickly on long legs, over the rocky ledges into the crevices. Although tied to the sea's margins, living in the area of salt spray, they are independent of the sea, even for breeding, and the female carries the young in a brood-pouch. Like their close relatives the woodlice, however, they must have moist conditions, and there seems little doubt that they are living under the kind of conditions that the ancestors of woodlice passed through before they became so completely terrestrial. Just below the level of the slaters the smaller crevices in the rocks are lined with very small periwinkles, the largest of them a bare quarter of an inch across. There are two species of them. The first sometimes lives so high up that it can seldom be wetted even by the spray, but it can survive for half a year out of water, its gill-chamber can act as a lung, and it is almost a terrestrial animal except that its larvae are pelagic. That is, they swim in the sea. The second species does not live so high up, cannot breathe air so well, cannot go for so long without water, but its young are born alive, and it would not entail a great deal of change to convert it into as completely a terrestrial animal as the land snail.

Just below this zone of the two small periwinkles, are the acorn barnacles, and in the first lines of barnacles we find a stunted leathery seaweed, looking under normal conditions as if dried up beyond hope of survival. It is, however, immersed, like the highest of the barnacles, by the highest of the spring tides. From here downwards, the barnacles become more numerous, are joined by limpets, mussels, other periwinkles, as well as, from about mid-tide level, by sea-anemones, sponges, crabs and all the rest of the animals we associate with the shore. From mid-tide level up to the upper limit of acorn barnacles, however, the beach does not support a very varied population, although the species that are there are represented by large numbers of individuals. This is especially true of the acorn barnacles. From mid-tide level to low-water neaps, anemones, sponges and others become more obvious, but it is largely between the level of the lowest of the neap-tide ebb and the extreme low-water springs that the multiplicity of forms is found. And for the most profitable shore-collecting, we look to the two periods, in spring and autumn, and especially in the spring, when the shore is uncovered to its maximum depth. Over these same zones, we pass successively the flat wrack, bladder wrack and toothed wrack, with the small red seaweeds coming in more and more as we pass from the lowest neaps to the lowest springs, until finally we are in the richest zone of all, the Laminaria-zone or the zone of the oar-weed, uncovered only at the lowest of the low-water springs, and even then only its inner margins uncovered completely.

CHAPTER THREE

NEW MIGHTY ATOMS

THE most numerous animals on the sea-shore are the
most obvious yet the least familiar—seen but not
recognised. They are as numerous as the sands of the
shore, and, indeed, in places, their cast shells often make
up that sand. They do not enter into our story to any major
extent although forms related to them have invaded the
land and the freshwaters in their myriads. In fact, in
numbers of species and populations they rival the fantastic
figures of the insects that swarm over the land and in the
fresh waters. They are the unicellular Protozoa, and although numerous on land, they are not truly terrestrial,
for they cannot live on dry land, but in all moist situations
including the bodies of all other animals. If we include
with them the unicellular plants, as well as those neither
one nor the other, the so-called plant-animals, then we
embrace not only those organisms which constitute the
basis of life in the sea—the so-called Pastures of the Sea,
but those responsible for many diseases both in the sea and
on land.

The Protozoa, very nearly the lowest forms of life, are
for the most part smaller than a pin's head. A large number of them consist simply of a naked protoplasm; but
many fashion their own shells, of lime or silica. Some make
a house of sand-grains or the minute cast-off shells of
others of their kind, often of exquisite beauty, appreciable
only under the microscope. In parts of the oceans, their
shells, raining down from the surface waters through long
ages have covered the sea-bed for thousands of square
miles. No part of the sea-bed anywhere is free of them. The

rocks forming the earth's crust are full of their remains, some strata, indeed, being made up almost exclusively of them. They show, in short, the widest possible diversity of shape, form, habitat and behaviour. Yet each is, approximately, the equivalent of a single cell of the body of one of the higher animals. And nothing could demonstrate more strikingly, than does their diversity of form and habit, the potentiality for almost infinite change within the range of the single cell.

One of these Protozoa, the Amoeba, early found its way into the text-books on biology as the modern representative of what used to be called "the primeval blob of protoplasm". According to the then current theory, living matter came into existence in much this form, aeons ago under circumstances which could only be surmised, to start the succession of life through the ages. To-day we realise that, in whatever manner life first came into being, it was in a form far simpler than that of Amoeba, or for that matter any protozoon. Amoeba delighted also the hearts of the early mechanists, for here at the base of the animal kingdom, they found not only the simplest unit of life—or so they thought—but the perfect living robot which moved and had its being entirely, or almost entirely, at the dictates of stimuli received from the environment. This view was further strengthened when someone found he could make artificial amoebae with a mixture of rancid oil and sand-grains, blobs of which moved and behaved to all intents and purposes like the living animals, except that they could not reproduce themselves.

We have travelled a long way since then. To begin with, simpler organisms still have been discovered, simpler even than bacteria. Concurrently, further researches have shown that the protoplasm of even a simple animal cell, whether the body of a protozoon or one of the cells comprising the bodies of the higher animals, is a highly organised unit. To return to Amoeba; it moves about in an irregular flowing manner engulfing solid particles for food, which the artificial amoebae were able to do also. On the other hand, the living organism could do what the robot could not: sort edible from inedible matter, digest it, adding parts of it to its own substance and rejecting the rest. Later, another investigator had the good luck to watch a large Amoeba chasing a smaller one, in a slow relentless pursuit which the smaller one sought to evade. This cast a new light on the supposed robot. Moreover, when a chase of this kind was filmed and the picture of it speeded up and projected, many times life-size, on to a screen, the impression made on the minds of the audience was not of one robot chasing another.

It may be perfectly true that such a chase can be analysed in terms of physics, chemistry and mathematics. It may be possible to explain the movements of Amoeba in terms of stresses and strains between two surfaces of different physical composition. Or to explain the impulse in the larger Amoeba, to move towards the smaller, in terms of a chemical attraction. When, however, the scene is speeded up to a pace with which we are more familiar, and when the size is magnified to proportions more nearly those of our own, the impression on the onlooker is startling. It can only be described in terms more applicable to human beings: that there is something sinister in the relentless pursuit by the large Amoeba; there is an appearance almost of cunning in the way it keeps on the trail of its victim. And in the victim there is, strange as it may sound, every appearance of fear, of an endeavour to throw its pursuer off the trail by taking evasive action. All this can be said of organisms less than a millimetre across, and supposedly very near to a basic unit of living matter.

All these appearances may be, and probably are, subjective, a delusion created in the mind of the observer. At these levels of life, although we can apply tests and carry out experiments, we are as far off really knowing what goes on in the body and in the experience of a single-celled animal. So the way is still open to speculation, and to hot debate between the mechanists and the vitalists—not that they do debate much now-a-days, for each is contemptuous of the other's point-of-view.

As I have said, the Protozoa do not appropriately concern us here. This digression, if such it be, has been deliberately introduced with two ends in view. The first is to emphasise how great is the appreciation to-day, as compared with the days of Darwin, say, of the great potentialities contained within the confines of even the simple microscopic cell. The second is to introduce another line of enquiry, in which this same great potentiality can be demonstrated, but more exactly, namely in the science known as Genetics, the study of heredity.

Genetics is concerned not only with the factors which make for stability in inheritance but also with those making for change. It is the study, therefore, not only of the molecular structure of the cell but also of the behaviour of those molecules. And since it has now been firmly established that changes in the gross structure and the habits of animals spring directly from changes or mutations in the molecular structure of the cells from which they are derived, no account of the evolution of terrestrial animals from marine ancestors, however superficial it may be, can ignore the evidence and implications of genetics.

The results of the study by the Austrian monk, Gregor Mendel, in the middle of last century, on crossing different varieties of garden peas, long remained in obscurity. When they finally came to light however, towards the end of the century, the knowledge Mendel had revealed gave a fresh outlook in biology. It also gave an impetus to new ideas gaining in the minds of other scientists, and the result has been that the science of genetics has grown so vast that only a specialist in it can do its findings justice. For our present purpose, however, even a superficial knowledge of its principles will suffice. There is one point I wish to make in this connexion—a point which, in my opinion, cannot be over-stressed. It is that all the diverse animal forms, alive to-day or that have ever existed, have arisen as simple mutations occasioned in the ultra-microscopic catalysts, the so-called genes, within the protoplasm of the living cell. Whether the result has been to produce an elephant or a jellyfish it is no more than the cumulative effect of minute changes over a vast period of time. This much can be reasonably supposed from the results of direct experiment. Changes in these excessively minute genes can be shown to have far-reaching effects, often leading to changes in the structure of an organ, or even to its complete loss.

A plant or animal cell consists of two parts, within the cell wall: the cytoplasm, or main body of the cell, and a central kernel, or nucleus. When a cell divides, the cytoplasm separates into two parts, to all appearances in the way one might break a piece of dough into two. The division is, however, preceded by a division of the nucleus, which takes place only after a complex chain of events, known collectively as mitosis, has been completed. Unlike the gross cleavage of the cytoplasm there is, in the division of the nucleus, a careful sorting out of its substance and a sharing of its parts between the two daughter cells. The first sign that a cell is about to divide is that threads appear in the nucleus. These because of their higher refractive index, stand out conspicuously from the nuclear sap in which they are embedded, so that they can be seen with, at least, the higher powers of the microscope. The usual method in the laboratory of making cell structure more conspicuous is, however, first to immerse the tissues to be examined in a stain or dye. The nuclear threads take up dyes more readily than the rest of the cell, and it was because, when thus treated, they showed up prominently as coloured bodies, that they were called chromosomes, literally coloured bodies. Each species of plant or animal has a constant and characteristic number of chromosomes in the nuclei of the cells of its body, and the relative lengths of these chromosomes is characteristic. In other words, the pattern of the chromosomes is the same for every member of the species.

Before the cytoplasm begins to divide, the wall bounding the nucleus breaks down and the nuclear sap comes into contact with the cytoplasm. From being a fluid, or at best a thin jelly, the sap hardens to form a spindle of fibres, and

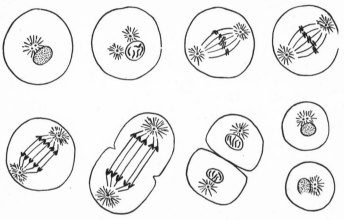

The living cell divides into two daughter cells.

each chromosome moves into position on one of these fibres and there becomes attached. Then each chromosome divides into two along its length and one half migrates to each end of the spindle. It seems that the fibres of the spindle contract and help to pull the chromosomes apart, but once the two halves have started to migrate that part of the fibre stretching between the two halves elongates to push them towards their respective destinations. Finally, when they have reached the opposite poles of the spindle, the two groups of half chromosomes rearrange themselves as they were before the division of the nucleus was begun. Then the spindle resumes the fluid or jelly form, reverting thereby to a nuclear sap; each group of chromosomes becomes embedded in a half of that sap, and a nuclear wall re-appears to enclose both sap and chromosomes. Two nuclei now exist where there was previously one, and the final phase of the division of the cell takes place. The cytoplasm divides to give two cells in place of the previous one, each with its cytoplasm, nucleus and chromosomes. Mitosis is followed by what has been erroneously called the resting stage. During this period of supposed resting, little change is seen in the nucleus but, in fact, the chromosomes are actively growing and reproducing themselves by splitting in two. After which the cell has once more the full complement of chromosome material, despite the fact that in the course of the division, the original material had been shared between the two daughter cells. The process comes very near to having the cake after eating it.

The division of the germ-cells is slightly different, and to mark this it is given a different name, meiosis. In the course of it, the number of chromosomes is reduced by a half. After this, there is a mitotic division, so that by the time the ovum and sperm are ready to come together in fertilisation, each possesses only a portion of the original chromosome material. The cells of the offspring to which the fertilised ovum gives rise will, as a consequence, possess new sequences and combinations of chromosome material, and although these have been derived partly from the maternal parent and partly from the paternal parent they differ from them both. To say that like begets like is true therefore in a general way only. No two members of a family or litter will be exactly alike, and none will be precisely like either parent.

The chromosomes are important since they carry the genes, the factors for inheritance. It is not possible to give

a more precise definition of them. Although the majority
of them cannot be seen even with the highest powers of the
microscopic, yet their presence can be demonstrated
mathematically and to a limited extent biochemically. In
one instance, however, they can be seen. The chromosomes of the salivary glands of the fruit fly, Drosophila, are
unusually large, half a milimetre long as compared with a
length of four-thousandths of a millimetre in the largest
chromosomes in the other body cells of Drosophila. In
these large chromosomes it is possible to see the genes with
the high powers of a microscope. There are five thousand
of them on a Drosophila-chromosome, and if we assume a
comparable number on the usual run of the smaller
chromosomes then we have to picture, for most species,
five thousand units or more for the transmission of physical
inheritance crowded on to a chromosome four-thousandths
of a millimetre long and even less across.

This brief survey of the behaviour and nature of the
chromosomes and their contained genes does less than justice to a science which in fifty years has come to dominate
the whole field of biology. Its findings have done more
than confirm Darwin's theory of organic evolution, they
have provided the means of explaining the very basis for
the changes by which organic evolution could have been
brought about. Although the practical application of
genetics is seen best in the selection of new varieties and
strains of domesticated plants and animals, its study
is in the realm of micro-biochemistry and mathematics.
Indeed, much of its material lies beyond the reach of the
techniques at present known, and many questions con-
cerning the nature and functioning of the genes remain
unanswered so far. So we have the paradox that while the
nature of the gene is mainly the subject of speculation, its
role can be demonstrated both theoretically and in practice. And no survey, however limited of organic evolution
can ignore its far-reaching influence.

Perhaps the two more remarkable things about the processes of mitosis and meiosis are, first, the complicated yet orderly mechanism by which the chromosomes are divided and shared out in cell-division. And, secondly, the fact that the chromosomes and the genes are capable of unlimited reproduction and growth. There is also the third thing, to which reference has already been made, but which cannot be too strongly emphasised, the incredibly small size of these factors for inheritance, which dominate and influence the lives of all living organisms from conception to death. Finally, the nucleus and its chromosomes have an inherent rhythm of activity.

The gene-complex, that is, all the genes, in a cell-nucleus, has been likened to a board of directors, who must work in harmony if the organisation they serve is to flourish or even to survive. The genes themselves are capable of mutation, but any change in one or a group of genes must not upset the harmony with the rest of the complex or the organisation cannot work. Most mutations are, in fact, lethal. In other words, a change in one or more genes in a complex throws out the balance of the group and a fatal disharmony afflicts the economy of the individual in which the change has occured. But on the rare occasions that such changes are harmonious the effect is to produce alterations, small or great in the structure of the organism they control. In addition to the gene-mutations, the chromosomes themselves can undergo changes. A portion of one chromosome may break away and become united with a neighbouring chromosome; or two chromosomes may join up and cross so that in the subsequent division of their substance there is a major re-grouping of that substance and of the contained genes. The combined effects of gene mutation, the regrouping of the genes in the break-up and joining up of chromosomes, together with the re-sortings that take place in the meiosis associated with sexual reproduction, give a very wide scope for structural changes within the chromosomes. There are other changes that can take place, but we need merely note that the effect of these is in principle the same as those already detailed: to produce changes in the structure of the organism.

When a species is living in a habitat to which it is suited, and with which it is in harmony, mutations of any kind and especially those that are large are to the disadvantage of the individuals in which they are manifest. If I am really comfortably seated in an arm chair any change of position is likely to be for the worse. A small change may not matter much and I may adjust myself to it; a large change in position or posture is likely to be unbearable. In a species well-adapted to its environment, mutations are apt to have this same effect; and where the changes are large the individual carrying them must find accommodation in another habitat or perish.

On the other hand, gene changes may not necessarily emerge at once, and a species may accumulate gene variations. When a change in the environment does take place these can emerge to give sufficient flexibility to respond to and meet those changes. A species so well adapted to a stable environment that it does not accumulate sufficient gene variations will become extinct if the environment is altered. In other words, a variable environment, like that we have examined between tide-marks, will engender variable genes, the best raw material for further evolution.

Although the science of genetics dominates the study of biology, and especially of evolution, it does not hold the answer to every question or problem in those fields. On the contrary, gene-changes merely present the raw material to be moulded. It is the forces which sift these changes, the natural selection as we call it that we are more concerned with here. It is possible to explain random changes in the gene fairly briefly. It is less easy to show how they give rise to changes in structure; and it is far less easy to demonstrate the full range of processes responsible for natural selection.

If the transition of the various groups of animals from the sea to the land is to be likened to a steeplechase, then to understand what is happening we need to know something of the abilities of those taking part. We need to know why some runners fail at the main obstacle, why some turn back, why others finish the course, and so on. Even then, our picture will not be complete without a passing acquaintance at least with the rules governing the race itself. This last is contained, in the sense in which we are now considering it, in the principles underlying organic evolution.

The theory of evolution has undergone many changes since it was first enunciated, but to-day it is fairly generally summed up in a simple formula: that organic evolution, or the derivation of existing forms of life from pre-existing forms, all having a common origin, is the result of random mutation acted upon by natural selection. It would be very easy to become lost in the intricacies of explanation of this seemingly simple formula. For our purpose it need only be recalled that all individuals of a species tend to vary. In spite of an all-round tendency for like to produce like, as already stated, no two individuals of a family, litter or brood are ever completely alike. In the main the differences are comparatively trivial, but if there are changes in the environment, then some individuals will be better suited to meet those changes. They will have the greater chance of surviving and perpetuating their advantageous features.

To accept the theory of organic evolution implies the recognition that all living matter is kin. Even without the theory we should be obliged to recognise that the protoplasm, whether of a simple one-celled organism or of any of the higher animals, does not differ fundamentally in its architecture or its chemistry. In the anatomy, physiology, habits and reactions to the environment of the individual animal, there are the same fundamental agreements. There are also the same tendencies towards hereditary stability, the same potentialities, qualitatively if not quantitatively, for change. In other words, there are the same probabilities that random variations may arise and the same possibilities for natural selection to act upon them. Why, then, we must ask, have some types of animals remained practically unchanged over a period of 300 million years or more, during which time the stock from which they sprang has given rise, along another line, to new forms, which die out after giving rise to still newer forms, and so on down to the present day? It is the story, once more, of the steeplechase, but more difficult to visualise and even more difficult to explain in detail.

CHAPTER FOUR

RACING FOR THE SHORE

IT must sometimes seem absurd, on the face of it, to suppose that the diversity of animals and plants living to-day should have originated in, and evolved from, ancestral forms of life so small and so simple as to be little removed from non-living matter. In the same way, it must seem absurd to suppose that an elephant can have anything in common with a jellyfish or man with a sea-urchin. On the other hand, nobody sees any cause for surprise that in a few thousand years, the human race, with little or no difference in the structure of the brain or in the other physical components of the body, should have progressed from making crude stone implements to the jet aeroplane and the atom bomb. All are, however, possible from the cumulative effects of small events and changes; and when we are dealing with the evolution of the animal kingdom, from its incredibly simple beginnings to the present day, we have to take another highly significant factor into consideration, the enormous span of time during which it has been accomplished.

The early writers on evolution were, perhaps, in error in laying too much stress on the big changes, and in the pre-supposing that catastrophic events were needed to produce them. The attitude to-day can be summed up in the remark that headlines do not make history. In other words, as in human affairs it is the everyday events, too small to be noted in the newspapers, that influence the course of history, the headline events representing the turning points only, so, in animal evolution we have to search closely for the causes of change. The cataclysm mentioned in a previous chapter, the furious natural phenomena of weather and other physical forces, and the spectacular rises and falls in populations, are more the headline events in the evolutionary story. The real causes of evolution are the everyday events, micro-cataclysms they could be called, that are responsible for the big changes. So, to understand what the modern discoveries in biology have to teach us, we have to search among the unspectacular things. More than anything else, we have to realise the tremendous and far-reaching effects brought about by minute changes and influences, by the re-grouping of molecules, by the effects of infinitesimal traces of catalysers, and the like. For fifteen thousand million years Nature has been splitting the atom, with results more enduring if less spectacular to our eyes than the explosions at Hiroshima, Bikini and Monte Bello.

Nobody can be certain exactly how a gene works, but one view, the one already expressed, is that it is a catalyst. The use of a catalyst, such as a gene, a hormone, a vitamin, or other subtle determiner, is a constantly recurring theme in modern biological research. A catalyst is any substance which influences change in other materials without itself undergoing change. Its influence can therefore be exerted when it is present in relatively small proportions, and this influence can be enduring. Moreover, minute changes in catalysts can be of differing levels of potency without increase in quantity. To understand the effect of the genes, and other phenomena governing the living organism, the full force of this must be appreciated, and I can think of no better way of emphasising it than by describing what must be a common scene in this modern world. The one I have in mind took place at a London railway terminus. Crowds of people were surging through the station and on to the escalators. Some wanted to move quickly, others wanted to take their time, as is usual. It so happened, at this moment, that the rule, normally followed, that those wishing to go slowly should stand on the right of the escalator so that those in a hurry could run down on the left, was suspended. Chaos resulted. A railway inspector, in uniform, stood at the foot of the escalator shouting: "Please keep to the right". A few obeyed, but not many, and the chaos was not perceptibly reduced. Then a policeman appeared and uttered the same words. As if by magic the crowd sorted itself out, and in a matter of seconds, order was restored.

The policeman suffered no change in the process. His influence continued as long as he stood there, and, for that matter, long after. He represented a minute quantity, one human molecule among thousands of others. He acted as a catalyst. The railway inspector also acted as a catalyst, but his influence was weaker, was of a different level of potency. It took longer to be effective and was probably less enduring.

We may take the analogy furnished by the policeman even further. In the course of human affairs, the armies, navies and air forces may be the agents of cataclysmic events, but the true course of modern human destiny, whether considered nation by nation, or over the human race as a whole, is determined very largely by its police, by the micro-catalysts, so to speak. But the actions of the fighting services take precedence in the headlines.

It was necessary to emphasise to this extent the place of the catalysts, and with them the other apparently insignificant influences and events in the biological field in order to correct our perspective. That done, we can pass to a review of the more obvious things that make for change and the means whereby these are met and countered. The micro-cataclysms include, so far as inter-tidal animals are concerned, those factors common to all animals, such as competition among themselves for food and for living space. Both these may be between members of the same species and also between members of different species occupying the same terrain. There is also the conflict and stress as between predator and prey. In addition we have such things more peculiar to marine organisms, such as changes in salinity and the effects of swirl and scour.

The micro-cataclysms are met and overcome by a marine animal, as by all others, mainly by occupying a comfortable niche, one to which it is well-suited, and which is not already occupied by another animal with which it is in competition. Or, in zoological terms, an ecological niche, may be represented by a particular place on a sand bank or a crevice in a rock, wherein the animal can maintain a balanced economy in relation to its environment. It is also one in which competition is at a minimum. In other words, a niche in which there is a favourable maximum, or optimum, as it is called, of security. Even within this ecological niche there is constant change, varying in degree, according to the particular niche, not only from changes in the physical conditions, but from rises and falls of the population of the species itself or in other species occupying the same or adjacent niche; and more especially varying according to the rises and falls in the numbers of the predators. And always there is the threat of greater and more general cataclysms from outside.

The first question naturally to arise from this is what determines that an animal shall occupy a particular niche. The general answer is that it will occupy the niche to which it is best suited or adapted. And having said that one is confronted with the need for saying what these adaptations are. That is a wide subject that must be deferred for the moment. The more immediately striking point is that animals do not differ from human beings, fundamentally, in the stresses and strains they must experience and in the means they must use to meet them. We can indeed use a human phraseology most appropriately to describe the total of these. We can, in truth, say that in the animal kingdom there is a constant striving for security; also, there is an everlasting search for a full life. There are other things besides, of course, but for the sake of simplicity we will keep to these two for purposes of further comparison.

The life of a human being is beset with difficulties. Some are personal, or individual, some are local difficulties. Others are national or racial difficulties, and finally there are the more widespread catastrophes, such as floods and drought, cyclones and hurricanes, earthquakes, wars, diseases and pestilence. These are met by adapting and adjusting one's way of life to meet the peculiar needs, temporary or of long duration, by co-operation with one's fellows, by using the services of other species, and by new inventions. Above all, and without which none of these things could be used, we are endowed with an inherent equipment for making adjustments to changing circumstances and dangers. Our own adaptations are largely the result of trial and error; even our deliberate and well thought out plans have to be subject to trial and error test, even if only by the use of models, trial tests, or rehearsals. Our inventions arise largely by accident. Indeed, it is arguable, although to do so here would be an inappropriate digression, that all human invention is in the end accidental; accidental against a background of knowledge, possibly, but accidental all the same. So the sum total of human adaptation—to which we normally give the name "progress"—is compounded of trial and error learning, and accidental discovery and invention, played upon, sifted and sorted, by a concatenation of natural circumstances, adverse or favourable. The result for the human race was briefly and simply expressed earlier on as the progress from making flint implements to making jet planes and atom bombs.

The same idea exactly underlines the biologist's appraisal of the forces of organic evolution as a whole, when he says that it is the result of random mutation acted upon by the pressure of natural selection. Random mutation is the equivalent of accidental change and the pressure of natural selection merely connotes the sifting and sorting by a concatenation of natural circumstances, adverse or favourable. In other words, human evolution springs from the same causes as the presumed evolution of the rest of the animal kingdom and is in principle no different. We are, however, more familiar with both the facts and the causes of human evolution and we know from this familiarity that accident played upon by circumstance has running through it a thread of continual striving towards an unknown goal. The course of this striving may be erratic, the striving itself may be blind, at least so far as any goal in the material world is concerned. Mostly its goal is described, by those who take the trouble to think about it and describe it, as the achievement of individual happiness, or even of group happiness, which is no more than the attainment of a balance between the organism and its environment. The human environment may be wider, compounded of psychical as well as physical things, but the principle is still the same. The extension of this argument belongs to the field of philosophy. The important thing here is the recognition of that underlying thread of striving in the field of random forces, for this helps us to understand, although not to explain, the two schools of thought in the biological field, the mechanistic and the vitalistic. The mechanist holds that all evolution is the result of blind chance—random mutation acted upon by natural selection; the vitalist sees a directiveness in organic evolution as a whole, a striving towards a goal, limited and undefined.

With few exceptions, all groups of animals have achieved some invasion of the land from an original marine habitat. Some have been more successful than others, but in all groups there is seen an apparent endeavour to press in to the shore, to reach up to high-tide mark or beyond, to penetrate the rivers, and, either by way of the shore itself, or by way first of the estuaries, then the rivers and finally the marshes, on to the land. Insects are unrepresented in the sea, except for a few species that have almost certainly returned secondarily to it, and there is no evidence in the earliest fossil insects of marine representatives. So we may picture them as having, very early, burst through the barrier between an aquatic and a terrestrial existence and flourished exceedingly. Moreover, in a general way, as we pass from one group to another of higher complexity, the tendency is more and more to forsake the marine life—or aquatic life—for one on land. The highest groups of animals and plants are all terrestrial, so that, taking it as a whole, there is a considerable justification for the impression that there has been a directive evolution with life on land as the goal. The fact that in all groups that have emerged and settled on land some members have secondarily gone back to the sea, such as turtles, penguins, seals and whales, does not necessarily invalidate or detract from such a viewpoint. Let us therefore at this stage accept the possibility that the vitalistic standpoint, held at the moment by a minority of biologists, may have something to commend it. We can then consider the causes and results in the light of modern research and make each our individual adjudication of the opposing schools of thought. Chief among these causes and results will be random mutations, natural selection, ecological niches, adaptations and inherent properties of living matter.

It may be as well to state now the primary requirements for life on land, as opposed to life in the sea. We find that in the more primitive groups of animals there is a marked tendency to a sedentary life. This, for an animal, is the first obstacle to a terrestrial existence. With plants it is different, since they have the property of manufacturing their own food from the sun, air and soil. An animal must either actively seek its food or have it brought to it. It can only be sedentary in an aquatic medium, in which food materials are transported by currents. Even spiders that have reverted, as some of them have, to an almost sedentary life, need the power of locomotion to construct their snares. They also need a means of locomotion for breeding, for the males and females to meet. For the rest, and excepting the hunting or wolf spiders and the jumping spiders, they mainly sit and wait for their food to be brought to them—on its own wings. This brings us to an even more urgent *sine qua non* of terrestrial life. In the lower animals the germ-cells, ova and sperm, are shed into the sea for random fertilisation to take place. On land this could not be effective unless, as some plants have achieved, there could be an airborne transportation of the germ-cells. So internal fertilisation, or something approximating to it, is essential. Internal fertilisation demands, in its effective expression, the segregation of the sexes. It is true that snails, slugs and earthworms are hermaphrodite and at the same time terrestrial, but the tempo of their lives is slow and this, coupled with their dependence on a moist habitat, suggests that they are only one degree beyond the aquatic stage, living as it were in a permanent state of being amphibious. There are snails living in the deserts but these do not upset the general statement, for the lives of desert snails are set at an even lower tempo and the need for moisture is as great. They merely find unusual ways of dealing with the situation.

As soon as members of a species become differentiated into males and females their troubles begin—a statement which few human beings would wish to dispute. Internal fertilisation makes impossible the production of stupendous numbers of offspring, as in the typical aquatic animal. The fewer offspring demand more attention if a sufficient number is to survive the natural hazards to ensure the perpetuation of the species. This leads to the need for parental care in some form or other, either by the building of nests, or the retention of the offspring within the maternal body until they have reached an advanced stage of development, both usually coupled with parental feeding in some form or other. Even the bringing together of the sexes for the breeding process is accomplished only by some form of courtship. All these things, and others not stated, require a high organisation of the body, especially of the muscles, and of the nerves to co-ordinate the activities of those muscles, as well as an elaborate system of blood-vessels to feed the muscles and nerves.

All these changes are therefore mutually inter-dependent. Any change towards an increased complexity in the muscles must be accompanied by comparable improvements in the nervous system and in the blood-vascular system, and so on. In other words, there could have been no life on land had there not been brought about the changes necessary to fit an organism for it. And because these are mutually dependent they must also be cumulative. It is possible to conceive, therefore, of an evolution being the result of purely random mutation, the cumulative changes supplying their own impetus to further changes.

In that event, we have to account for some groups of animals having progressed up to a certain point and no further, even though they may have been longer in existence than other groups that have become more specialised. In other words, we have to say why the backward ones have been held back. There is no general answer to this, except in the vaguest terms, and the only way to obtain even a moderately satisfactory answer is to take each in turn and examine it on its merits. Before we can attempt this there are several things that must be made clear. One of these is the question of what is a primitive animal and what is a specialised one. These words are in constant use by zoologists. They have occurred already in this text, and while the zoologist may know what he means—though this is by no means always certain—other people may not always be so clear. I cast a doubt on the zoologist's being sure because of instances such as the following. In a book published in recent years, an otherwise competent marine zoologist spoke of a certain species of barnacle as being "highly generalised". It is very plain that all living barnacles are highly specialised. Indeed, the geologists have been hunting for the fossil remains of a generalised barnacle for a very long time. If only they could find one it would shed a much desired light on the ancestry of the barnacles as a whole, which at the moment is anything but clear.

Another example must be given. The duckbill or platypus, of Australia, is always spoken of as the most primitive living mammal, which indeed it is. At the same time, it is also referred to as a highly specialised form. "Primitive", in its dictionary meaning, pertains to the beginning or origin. Yet the duckbill is far removed from the original mammals, although it has certain features in common with them. The word is used therefore in a relative sense, implying a shade of meaning which could be misleading.

Imagine a man whose hobby is joinery. We can picture him in his workshop. Before him is a pile of timber, in planks. He is an entirely free agent and it is open to him whether he shall make a bookcase, a wardrobe, a dining table or a kitchen dresser. Or it may be there is need for something less refined, say a hen-house, a bicycle stand or a wheelbarrow. On the other hand, his fancy may, at that moment, run to something smaller, such as book-ends, a tea-tray, letter rack or picture frame. The timber is his raw material, and as long as it is raw material he has an almost limitless choice of what he will make from it. Let us now suppose that he decides to make a bookcase. He saws a

number of pieces of wood, planes them, puts them together to make a box-like structure, the carcase as it is
called. Now, at this stage he can still change his mind. The
carcase can be used to make ultimately a wardrobe, or a
bookcase, or a china-cabinet, a set of lockers, a large filing
cabinet. At all events his choice is more limited than before, but the carcase is still generalised; and changes in its
structure are still relatively easy.

Let us now suppose he settles, at this stage on a wardrobe. He proceeds to make the doors, the shelves, a place
for the coat-hangers, a rack for shoes, a drawer for collars,
handkerchiefs and so on. He fits it with rails, handles, a
lock, a mirror and all the usual fittings. It has now become
a special piece of furniture. If now the joiner changes his
mind and wishes to have a bookcase instead of a wardrobe, it is difficult, if not impossible, to convert. It can only
be done by breaking what has been created, stripping the
wardrobe of its fittings, its racks, drawers and the rest,
back to the carcase. Even, then, the chances of making a
really satisfactory bookcase are not good.

There is another point to be emphasised. Not only is the
wardrobe a special piece of furniture but it must occupy a
particular place, a niche. Its proper place, or niche is in the
bedroom, or the dressing room; or possibly in a cloakroom or an entrance hall. It is therefore a special piece of
furniture with a special niche, although the niche may
be variable within narrow limits, namely the bedroom,
dressing room, cloakroom or entrance hall. The limits are
narrow in the sense that it would be out-of-place in a
kitchen, a bathroom, a dining room and so on. It would
not be fitting in those places, it would not be fulfilling its
function, it would be in the way; and the upshot would be
that it would soon be banished from such places.

We may go further with this special niche: suppose the
wardrobe is triangular in plan, it will fit only into a
corner. One can think of other circumstances in which a

wardrobe could be so constructed that it would fit neatly into one particular corner of a particular room. It has now become a highly specialised piece of furniture. It can be tolerated in that one place only, in that particular niche. If the owner moves house, into one of those buildings in which the rooms have rounded corners, then the wardrobe is entirely out of place. The surroundings, or environment as it is now necessary to call them, have changed and there is no place for the specialised piece of furniture.

It could happen that instead of the specialised corner wardrobe, the joiner made one that was rectangular, but, filled with enthusiasm, he ornaments and decorates it, with carvings and flourishes so that it matched, or fitted in with the rest of the furniture in the room. If the rest of the furniture should be changed, this highly specialised wardrobe would no longer fit in with the rest. He would then discard it in favour of another that matched the rest of the furniture. In such a case, the wardrobe would either be destroyed, or allowed to stagnate in a lumber room, or it might be transported to a bedroom in another house where it matched more nearly the rest of the furniture. Using zoological terms, the wardrobe would become extinct, linger in an out-of-the-way habitat, or would have migrated (or been made to migrate) into another niche, or another environment.

Briefly, the more generalised the wardrobe, the longer it is likely to remain in use and the greater variety of positions (or niches) it can be made to occupy. Also the more readily can its shape be altered to serve a particular purpose or room. The more highly specialised it is, the narrower the range of functions it can fulfil, the fewer the places it can conveniently occupy and the more likely is it to be discarded the moment there is a radical change in circumstances.

Species of animals and plants follow the same lines as this hypothetical wardrobe, in the way they are evolved and in the fate meted out to them as circumstances remain constant or undergo change. Generalised they can readily give rise to new types, or species. Specialised they readily suffer under any change of environment, and either become extinct, or are relegated to a backwater, in an ecological or biological sense, or survive by migrating into an environment in which conditions approximate to those in which they lived formerly. The difference between a wardrobe and a living organism is that the latter has a greater inherent potentiality for adaptability. A wardrobe can be altered by the joiner, an animal can be altered by mutation; or, rather, its offspring can be so altered; and the comparison between the two is not a just one in that an attempt is being made to compare a static object with one that is essentially dynamic, and moreover capable of reproducing itself. In addition to structural or behavioural changes that may arise from the random mutations, an organism has an inherent adaptability, of parts of the body, and through them of the whole body. Nevertheless the comparison still has a point to it.

It might have been possible to replace the story of the joiner and his stock of wood, leading up to the making of the wardrobe, with a similar story of the evolution of an animal species, but for the fact that the raw materials of evolution are largely hypothetical and so too are the generalised types of animals. Even had this not been the case, I would still have preferred to use the human analogy, for two reasons. The first is that it is the more familiar and therefore more intelligible to the non-biologist. The second is, that by stressing the parallelism between human behaviour and human affairs generally, it may be possible to lessen an isolationism to which even the zoologist is all too readily given. What we do and how we behave are at one with the activities and behaviour, in a broad sense, of the rest of the living world. And as soon as we take cognisance of this, the whole field of biology becomes more understandable and intelligible, and so, conversely, do our own activities and behaviour. Furthermore, we can accept this close tie without any loss of dignity.

Nowhere in the total field of life is the close kinship between the human and non-human worlds more apparent than in a comparison between human inventions and animal structures. There is nothing new under the sun. The needle and thread were being used in the animal kingdom before ever man walked the earth. So was the periscope, the telescope, radar, echo-location, the caterpillar track, the Schnorkel apparatus. Houses were being built, lawns laid out, gardens planted, walls painted or distempered, by one species of animal or another. The list could be endless. There are, of course, obvious exceptions. No animal cooks its food, and man's mastery of fire is unique and one of the reasons for his having been able to parallel Nature's achievements. The wheel is not greatly in evidence in nature, and one can only assume that this limiting form of locomotion would have been eliminated by natural selection had it ever arisen in the form in which we use it. But the principle of the wheel is used widely. This whole subject is a wide one, capable of endless study. It is mentioned here merely to make the point that there is this coincidence between our own world and that of animals in general.

It could be argued that there is only a limited number of ways in which a particular problem can be solved, therefore there must be this coincidence. Also, that whereas each "invention" is found in one or at most a few animal species, man has them all, or will have them all in time. In answer to the first objection it is remarkable that the animal and human inventions should in most, if not all, cases be so very alike, when differences would not necessarily have made either unworkable. It is also remarkable that we find, where the evidence has been preserved, that they have been reached by the same steps. In fact, the whole appearance is of the human mind reflecting a synthesis of a creative impulse.

There is a further parallel I wish to draw. I have spoken of the steps in the evolution of animal structures and human inventions being difficult to find. One of the strongest arguments against the theory of organic evolution is that evidence, either in fossil remains or in any other way, of the generalised ancestral forms is difficult to come by. The same is precisely true in regard to human inventions. In the history of the invention of the aeroplane, merely to take a topical example, it would be difficult, even at this date so close to the start of the age of aviation, to find the generalised types of plane from which the wide diversity of types we know to-day sprang. The first types in any evolutionary sequence are simple and generalised, few in number and have a tenuous hold on life. Two things can happen. They may succeed in giving rise to improved types, or they may not. If the first, the success of the new types inevitably causes the early demise of their forerunners, which accordingly suffer extinction. The others die out because they are similarly outmoded.

Or to go back to our wardrobe. There must be millions of wardrobes in Britain, of all shapes and sizes, yet who can tell what the first wardrobe ever made looked like, where it is now, when it was made, and whether it was evolved from some pre-existing form of furniture? So is it with types of living organisms. In spite of the vast number of fossils known and examined, early generalised types are few and far between, which is precisely what we should expect if the evolution of living organisms is like that of human machines. So for most of our knowledge, and this applies no less to the subject we have in hand, we are compelled to fit together what meagre clues we can to reconstruct the picture.

CHAPTER FIVE

PARIAHS OF ZOOLOGY

IN the Middle Ages, it was a strongly-held notion that everything on land had its counterpart in the sea. So we had the sea-cow, sea-horse, sea-dog or dogfish, sea-urchin or sea-hedgehog, even the sea-maiden or mermaid, and the old books contain many crude drawings expressing this idea. There are depicted cows with webbed feet, horses with foaming manes and seal's flippers and dogs with gaping mouths showing well-developed canine teeth and bodies ending in fish-tails. The task of the writer on natural history would have been infinitely lightened had this really been the case. For example, in writing about a familiar subject such as a hedgehog one may assume that no descriptive explanation is necessary before proceeding with the narrative. And when we talk about a sea-hedgehog, or, as it is usually called, a sea-urchin, a picture of it can be presented with a minimum of words. It is otherwise with, say, the sea-gooseberry. First, one must explain that it is an animal, not a plant. Then it must be described, and nothing of its anatomy or appearance can be referred to in familiar terms without fear of misleading the reader. It helps nothing to call it by its alternative name, comb-jelly. If anything that is even more mystifying. So it is with most of the lower animals, especially those that live in the sea and have no counterpart on land.

Everyone is familiar with a sponge—in the bathroom; but that is the equivalent of saying that anyone familiar with a hambone knows what a pig looks like. And when I say I have been studying sponges on the coast of Devon, most people look at me in surprise: for them sponges belong only to the Mediterranean. The position has improved in the last thirty years, since the teaching of biology became more general in schools. Perhaps more surprising, even the average zoologist finds something rather amusing in one who has spent his life trying to study sponges. Vosmaer, the eminent Dutch Spongologist, evidently found the same thing, for he described sponges as the pariahs of zoology.

The Tower of Babel may have been built in Biblical times, but we have gone on building replicas ever since, and one of the best replicas has been fashioned by the scientist who prides himself on his use of a precise terminology. Of the many examples of the inability of the scientist to use or agree upon a lucid terminology, one was set when he accepted, for the living beast, the age-old and universally accepted name "sponge", the name used for its dead fibrous skeleton in the household. He would, of course, never say he was growing loofahs when he is growing gourds. Perhaps the fault goes back to the Ancient Greeks.

At all events, the sponge of commerce, fished since the time of the Ancient Greeks, if not before, and, since 1841, in the West Indies, is the fibrous skeleton of a most un-animal-like animal. In life, the interstices of this skeleton are filled with a soft flesh, the whole covered with a tough skin, yellow if the beast is growing out of the light, purple if exposed even to the feeble rays filtering down through several metres. The main fishing grounds are the Mediterranean, where the best quality sponges grow, and the West Indies, but they also occur throughout the tropical and subtropical seas. Elsewhere they are fished locally but the quality of the fibres is not as good as in those taken on the two main grounds.

The commercial sponges belong to a handful of species out of the five thousand or more known throughout the world. The remainder are everywhere, from the shore down to the greatest depths, ranging in size from little more than a pin's head to six feet or more across and weighing over a hundredweight. In places, even on parts of our own coasts, they are the more conspicuous animal, covering the rocks with splashes of crimson, tan, yellow, green or white, sometimes several square yards in area.

It is my invariable reply, when asked by would-be collectors how to recognise a sponge, that anything they find looking like nothing else on earth is likely to be a sponge. This is less facetious than it sounds; and if applied in a broader sense it is even more true. Sponges have been in existence for at least 500 million years, and, moreover, so far as we can tell, they seem to have changed little in that time. In spite of the fact that they are the pariahs of the science of zoology, they can make many important contributions to that science. So many, indeed, that it is not easy to select those most appropriate to our present purpose.

The first question we are prompted to ask is: If all parts of the animal kingdom have arisen from a common stock, why have sponges remained relatively unchanged from almost the beginning of time? The question could, of course, be asked for other groups of animals, to varying degree, but in none so strikingly as this group. If evolution is the result of random variation acted upon by natural selection, we can pertinently ask: Is there any evidence that sponges are less subject to random variation than other groups of animals; or are they less subject to the effects of natural selection? Before answering these questions, it will be profitable to pose, and dispose of, another question: Why have sponges, that have migrated far up the beach, towards dry land, and have sent representatives, the freshwater sponges, into every river and lake throughout the world, never obtained a footing on dry land? Or, again, why has this group of animals, so highly successful in its own sphere, and so enduring in time, remained almost completely static?

My hypothesis is that this is partly because they have been subject to a random variation expressed in characters that have no functional value, and upon which natural selection has little or no effect. They have, probably almost from the beginning, been endowed with a peculiar type of skeleton. This is subject to almost infinite variation, and that, for the rest, the body proper is sufficiently plastic that natural selection has little or nothing to work upon. There are, however, genetical reasons also, as we shall see.

Alternatively, we may see in this some of the conditions under which natural selection operates, by examining, as in this instance the reasons why it has to a great extent, failed to operate. Sponges have remarkably few enemies. They are eaten by sea-slugs and by one or two sea-snails, but the extent is small and sponges have remarkable powers of regeneration, so that the inroads made by enemies have little effect. They are also virtually free of disease, so far as we can tell, although some years ago the commercial sponge stock of the West Indies was decimated, possibly by a fungal disease. They have an unlimited supply of food, since this consists of finely microscopic particles of dead matter and, we have reason to believe, bacteria. The possibility that they are able to feed on bacteria may account for the freedom from disease, and certainly sponges grow to the greatest size and are in greatest profusion in harbours and estuaries where the water is polluted with sewage and garbage, and, presumably full of bacteria. Since food is everywhere, there is no need of special locomotary organs to assist in a search for it, and without the means of locomotion internal fertilisation, a necessary concomitant of emergence on to dry land is absent.

Sponges live by drawing water through minute pores in the skin, passing it through the body and ejecting it through a number of crater-like vents. In its passage through the body, oxygen and food are taken from it, and when the water is ejected it carries away the waste products. No amount of change in structure towards that of a terrestrial animal would be operative as long as the animal is tied so closely to water by this one feature of its economy. Even so, if our theories about organic evolution have any validity, we can suppose that there may have been some among the first multicellular animals that had much in common with our present day sponges, and that they must have progressed beyond that state.

It may be, of course, that the main stock of the animal kingdom arose in some entirely different way, and that the ancestral sponges took a different line from the start. There is no means of knowing for certain: the proof lies buried in the past, and anyone propounding an alternative view is doing precisely what I am doing, theorising. We are always up against two unfortunate but hard facts, that while life may originally have generated 1500 million years ago, as is now believed, the fossil record starts with the Cambrian rocks 500 million years ago, when all but the higher vertebrates were already in being.

The plastic nature of sponges to which I have just referred can be best understood by their powers of dissociation and regeneration. If a piece of sponge is squeezed in a bag of fine bolting silk, a milky fluid oozes through the silk. Drops of this, falling into a glass dish containing seawater, and examined under the microscope, are seen to consist of a large number of separate sponge cells. The cells of the tissues have been dissociated from each other. Settled on the bottom of the dish, they lose their individual shapes. Each takes on an irregular outline, and begins to wander about in an erratic manner. As time goes on the cells join up into small groups, of half-a-dozen to a score, each group of cells coalescing, taking on an irregular outline, and, in turn, wandering about. The large groups pick up isolated stragglers, or join up with other larger groups, until after 48 to 72 hours, small masses visible to the naked eye can be seen at the bottom of the dish. In a fortnight, young sponges as large as a pea are formed, capable of growing and, in three months, of producing their own larvae.

The first time I did this experiment was at the Aquarium of the London Zoo, using one of the sponges then growing in large numbers on the beds filtering the sea-water for the exhibition tanks. In the later stages, one need observe the progress of the experiment at long intervals only. With time on my hands, I tried a number of other experiments. For example, I took a dozen of sponges, which belonged all to the same species, and sewed them together with a needle and thread, merely to ensure that they remained in close contact, then put them back in an aquarium. In a fortnight they had joined up and overgrown the thread everywhere, so that I had one perfect large sponge instead of twelve.

The sponges were everywhere on the filter beds, their shapes differing somewhat according to whether they were growing in still water or running water, or any variation of these. When transplanted from one spot to another on the beds, the shape altered slowly to that typical for the conditions obtaining in that particular situation. The best effort at accommodation was by one which I turned upside-down in a thick watch-glass. This particular sponge, like so many, was in the form of a hemisphere, with half-a-dozen vents grouped on its upper surface. It exactly fitted the watch-glass when it was inverted, and theoretically, and probably in practice, although this was difficult to ascertain, the vents were no longer functional and the life-giving current of water through the body of the sponge was stopped. In any case, within a week, the edges of the sponge had grown out and hermetically sealed the body of the beast within the watch-glass. What was formerly the under surface, injured when the sponge was removed from its support in the filter bed, was now completely healed

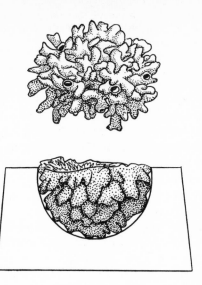

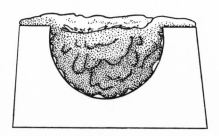

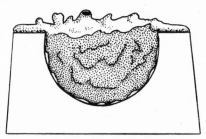

A sponge turned upside down re-organises
itself. (The watch-glass is shown diagram-
matically.)

and covered with a smooth skin. So far as one could see, the sponge could now no longer feed, and any respiration must be through the healed surface, although this had no openings to take in or eject a stream of water. During the next two weeks, the body being translucent, it was possible to watch the wholesale reorganisation taking place within it. One could watch new water canals being formed and, reaching up to the now upper surface, breaking through to form fresh vents. When I was compelled by circumstances to conclude this experiment, the sponge was well on the way to being completely reorganised and functional. In other words, there had been a complete inversion of the internal organisation as a result of being turned upside down.

Although these and other similar experiments show what can be done artificially, it is also the case that in all species of sponges, at some time or another, use is made in the natural state of similar readjustments and regeneration. In many species it is almost a normal procedure. The young of the Crumb-of-Bread sponge, for example, one of the commonest between tide-marks over a large part of the world, form thin, almost transparent encrustations on the rocks. At an early age, they are from a half-inch to an inch across, irregular in outline, coating the surface of the rock in groups. In that condition they look like larger editions of the small wandering masses which regenerate from the cells pressed through bolting-silk. By suitably marking them, it can be shown that they also move about, to a limited extent and as they wander their shape changes. As they move about, two of them may come into contact and join up completely, or a piece of one may part company with the rest of the crust and move off to join up with a neighbour. Eventually the whole group may join up to form one crust of very irregular outline, or several crusts more or less rounded at the margins, and finally, with little more movement reach the adult stage.

It becomes evident, the more one sees of their regenerative behaviour, that the plasticity of the tissues and the power of re-growth tends to be lost with age, but that small pieces broken off, artificially or by wave-action during storms, behave as real offspring, in that they are capable of a rejuvenescence. A close relative of the Crumb-of-Bread sponge, living between tides on our coasts, often bears a number of fingers. These may be broken off in heavy storms, and the beach may be littered with their fragments, all showing signs of regeneration, each fragment becoming a new sponge. Such reproduction by fragmentation may be called involuntary, but there are other species that use what may be called voluntary fragmentation.

I came across an extreme form of this accidentally, and the story of the discovery and its sequel is illuminating in several particulars. It starts with some 500 specimens of the common Purse sponge, collected by Lt-Cdr A. J. Cobham, R.N., some years ago and sent me for examination. Purse sponges, white, grey or cream in colour, shaped like flattened purses and measuring from half-an-inch to two-and-a-half inches in height, grow between low-water neaps and mean low-water springs, and thereafter more sparsely, down to extreme low-water springs. In polluted harbour waters they may grow to comparatively enormous size. In such situations and also on more favoured beaches on exposed rocky coasts they may be present in tens of thousands over a few hundred yards of beach.

This is a sponge very familiar to the student of zoology and its picture frequently appears in the text-books, where it is always depicted as a simple pouch, somewhat vase-shaped—invariably drawn the wrong way up. Even the simple outline is wrong. So, although I had known this sponge over a long period of years, I had yet one elementary lesson to learn from the preliminary study of these 500 specimens, for having laid them all out on the table before me, it struck me that a minority, and that a small one, had the simple shape shown in the text-books. The rest were folded and twisted upon themselves to a remarkable extent. The elementary lesson here is that a pre-conceived idea, implanted by the text-books in one's student days, may cause one to overlook, during the subsequent years, something which should be obvious. The next thing I learned was that it was possible to lay them out in series and to demonstrate that what we had here was a process of reproduction by fragmentation. At one point on its margin, the sponge would grow out and the new growth would fold over on to the main body. A line of weakness would then develop along the line of the fold, and along this the tissues would split, the newly-grown portion would then come away from the main body, develop its own stalk and start life as a new and completely functional sponge. It was possible also to demonstrate that this could happen in seven different ways. Of these the most remarkable was that in which a line of holes appeared in succession across the equator of a sponge, like the perforations on a postage stamp. Ultimately, the slender bridges between the holes would give way and the outer half of the sponge would fall away to grow into a new sponge, the injury on both halves healing over.

The story was all there in the half-a-thousand specimens preserved in alcohol laid out on the table before me. What I had to establish was whether this was an optical delusion, so to speak; whether I had not merely laid them out in series that conformed to what I thought may have taken place. In other words, it was necessary to be absolutely sure that this did take place in real life. I went to my favourite beach in Torbay, where Purse sponges are abundant, and there surely enough, they showed this same folding and twisting. I saw the same thing in Devonport Dockyard, Portsmouth Harbour, and a number of other places around the coast. At Torbay, I marked a number of specimens and made drawings of their outlines, to keep watch for any changes in the shape and for the time when the fragmentation would take place. In other words, nothing would suffice but that I should see the fragmentation actually taking place.

For a fortnight no change took place in the marked specimens, although they were well folded and seemed on the verge of fragmentation when I first found them. Then it was necessary to return to London. So began the long search which lasted three years. During that time I marked numerous specimens on the rocks at Torbay and visited them whenever possible, which amounted to an aggregate of about two months in each of the three years mainly in week-ends. Whenever possible, I watched at other points on the coast, but always with the same result. Finally, at the end of a three years' search, confirmation came, in a few all-too-brief minutes. As has already been said, the uppermost limit of the Purse Sponge coincides almost exactly with the low-water mark of the shallowest neap tides. On this Sunday afternoon, being near the shore, I had decided to take a look at the rocks, although it was the period of neap tides, and not very favourable. The tide had just started to flow when I saw a few Purse sponges hanging from the roof of a small chamber between the rocks, and one of them had the shape of an hour-glass. It was just possible to get down on to a small edge of rock, over which the water was already beginning to rise, and to watch the waist of the hour-glass lengthen, growing more and more slender until it was as fine as cotton. Touching the lower bulb of this hour-glass gently with my finger was sufficient to detach it from the parent body, and had it been possible to stay longer I could have seen it fall naturally. Unfortunately, the water was already threatening to cut me off and the way back to the top of the beach was over a mass of rock, with the gullies between already filling up.

While paying particular attention to this one specimen, however, it was possible to take note of others in the same cavity in the rock. One hour-glass shaped specimen had already divided and the outer half lay on the seaweed below. A third had divided across its equator as cleanly as though cut with a pair of scissors. The outer half of this also lay on the seaweed below the parent body. Already the split surface was healing and a stalk beginning to grow out. This one I was able to take back and keep in an aquarium, and watch the stalk grow to normal shape and size.

To carry the story to its end, and to answer an obvious question springing from it, it should be said that repeated attempts to watch the fragmentation of the Purse Sponge in an aquarium were unsuccessful. In any congregation of this sponge there are a few individuals that exceed the average size quite considerably. These do not fragment in the same way but at certain times break up irregularly and disintegrate, and from my limited observations it would appear that this precedes an epidemic of the normal fragmentation. If this guess—for it is no more than that— is correct, then the fragmentation of the normal sized sponges is set in train by hormone or other ectocrine given off by the larger disintegrating sponges. And it probably always occurs on a rising tide at the shallowest neap tides, when the sponges are hidden from view. In other words, it takes place under circumstances almost impossible to reproduce artificially.

There is nothing remarkable in the story of the Purse Sponge. It is the common lot of the biologist that convincing evidence, upon even such a small matter as the one recounted here, is difficult to come by, and as often as not is the result of chance discovery at the end of a long search. The many gaps in our knowledge of marine animals, which must become only too evident as our narrative proceeds, will be understandable from this one personal experience, as well as from others to be given later.

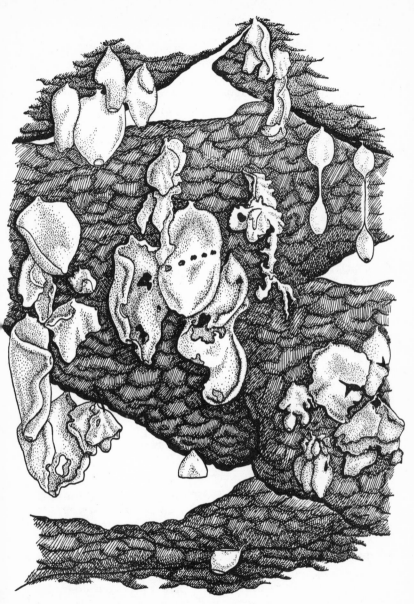

Purse sponges, on an overhanging rock, breaking up to form new sponges.

There is nothing new in the idea of organisms multiplying by fragmentation. It is a phenomenon familiar to all gardeners in taking cuttings; and several groups of animals, in addition to sponges, take cuttings of themselves, so to speak. The interest, rather, lies in understanding its mechanism. The observations and experiments given here do, at least, give us a clue to this. And two more first-hand experiences may take us a step further in the understanding.

There was on the beach at Torbay another common littoral sponge, a White Lace Sponge, forming small cushions composed of a tight network of minute tubes. It was most plentiful at mid-tide level. Further down the beach, uncovered only on a good spring tide, was one exactly like it except that it was coloured red. Each of these formed the typical small regenerative masses when squeezed through silk. Since the white and the red forms appeared to be no more than simple varieties of the same species, would cells from each come together to form one regenerative mass? The experiment had already been made of trying to induce the cells from two sponges belonging to different species to join up and it had failed. The cells separated out into distinct masses, true to type. In this series of experiments, two White Lace Sponges growing side by side, and therefore probably from the same brood, were taken and one was stained blue with a harmless dye. When their component cells were intermingled they formed regenerative masses in the minimum time, the blue cells could be seen mingling with the white. Next, two White Lace Sponges were taken from opposite ends of the beach, almost certainly belonging to two separate broods. Again, one was stained blue. When intermingled, their cells tended to come together, at first showing distinct groups of blue and white but slowly, as if their resistance to each other were gradually broken down by familiarity, they intermingled completely as in the cells from sponges of the one brood. But they took longer to do so. When cells from the red and the white varieties were intermingled, they slowly separated out into small masses of two distinct colours, red and white.

There is another littoral sponge, the Sea Orange. It is spherical, one to two inches diameter, orange or yellow in colour, its body composed of an outer muscular rind and an inner soft flesh. At certain seasons a number of warts appear on the surface of its body, and these, in time, become spherical, later growing a stalk and finally becoming star-shaped. They are non-sexual reproductive bodies, usually called buds. We know that they are composed of cells migrating from the inner soft flesh, through the outer rind, to form the star-shaped buds. To see what would happen, I took a small quantity of the inner flesh and squeezed it through silk. At the end of a fortnight, the usual regenerative mass had formed but it was star-shaped, double the size of a normal bud, somewhat flaccid, but a fair representation of the normal reproductive body for that species. Although the conditions were abnormal, the cells had made a creditable attempt to perform their task normally.

Sponges have no central nervous system. At the best they possess isolated nerve-cells to control the functioning of the body. At all times, and especially when dissociated, the tissue cells are capable of a group action, of co-operating towards a definite end and for a clearly defined purpose, and there must, obviously, be a means of accomplishing this. Why, for instance, when a portion of a Purse Sponge breaks away from the main body leaving two raw edges should the cells in the region of the two lines of injury spontaneously work to heal the injuries? Why, also, when that portion has fallen away should other cells automatically move into position to form a stalk, in anticipation of the needs of the individual as a whole? We can only surmise that they are communicating their "intentions" to each other, as surely as when we speak to one another, and that the need which they must supply has been signalled. We can only say, arguing from what has already been investigated in other fields, that communication between them is by the secretion from individual cells of minute traces of chemicals, the hormones or something akin to them, in such minute traces as to baffle detection. They are chemical words, as definite and as effective as our spoken words, and equally transient. Above all they are of molecular proportions.

CHAPTER SIX

VARIATIONS ON A SIMPLE THEME

THE fishermen of Japan and the Philippines have a wholesome respect for the sea-wasp because of its ability to inflict a severe sting, but to the inhabitants of the Gilbert Islands they constitute a delicacy. Sea-wasps, jellyfish of the type known as Carybdeids, have four-sided bells, with flattened sides, and with tentacles hanging from each corner of the bell. Apparently when weather conditions are normal, sea-wasps appear in the surface waters around the Gilbert Islands, at predictable intervals, coming into the shallows seven days before the full moon. They are then caught and eaten. The method of preparation is to scrape away the bell and the tentacles with a blunt knife and boil what is left, which is mainly the reproductive organs. They can also be dried in the sun, hung out on long lines like so much washing, and stored. When treated in this way they must be reconstituted before use, after which they are friend in fat. Boiled without being first dried they are said to taste like tripe. Fried, they resemble pork crackling. The sea-wasp fishery would hardly be profitable if the jellyfish were of the size we usually encounter round our own coasts, but in the Pacific jellyfish may be seven feet across, so that even allowing that their bodies are mainly water there still remains enough protein to make it worth the trouble. All jellyfish occur in shoals, require no special skill in the catching, so this particular harvest of the sea can be gathered with little effort—by those who find it palatable.

There must be remarkably few culinary uses for jellyfish or any of their relatives, although it appears that the

Japanese themselves concoct a dish from the jellyfish found round their own shores. To most people, a jellyfish has one outstanding characteristic: it can sting. For this reason, it is normally given a wide berth. Even when it is lying stranded on the beach, already half-way to disintegration in the sun's rays the finder will examine it by turning it over with a stick, or by prodding it with the toe of the shoe. The sting of a wasp is effective for some hours after the death of the insect and it is possible that the sting of a jellyfish in like manner remains operative after the rest of its body has relinquished its hold on life. So far as I know, there has been no considerable research to determine this, nor to determine for how long the stinging cells remain viable after the dissolution of the surrounding tissues. Most of us prefer to leave the question for some future investigator—a sound judgement. For a sting from unintentional and usually unsuspected contact with jellyfish, even the comparatively innocuous Medusa of our temperate waters, can be a sufficient inconvenience, although it is in practice less troublesome to sustain than the angry appearance of the red rash on the skin might lead the onlooker to suppose. In warmer waters more virulent forms have contributed to the evil reputation of the jellyfishes as a whole. In particular one recalls the Bluebottle of Australian waters, and stories of death from its stings. Even here, the virulence of the sting seems to have been exaggerated in the popular mind. Deaths from the sting of the Bluebottle have occurred but detailed records are hard to come by. Doubtless they are to be found in medical case-books and journals. It does appear, however, that young children, people of all ages in a state of ill-health and, especially, those who panic, are more susceptible to the poison. In other words, the virulence seems comparable to that of our adder, whose bite can under similar circumstances prove fatal but in most cases proves no more than a distressing but temporary injury.

The name Medusa was first applied to the species of jellyfish most commonly seen round our coasts. Medusa was the mortal daughter of the gods, famed for her personal charms and the beauty of her locks. She violated the sanctity of the temple of Athena and paid for her misdeeds by having her tresses turned into serpents which petrified those who looked on them. The simile is apt so far as the smaller marine animals are concerned. At least, on contact with the jellyfish's tentacles they are paralysed, and later engulfed in the elongated mouth that hangs like a handle from the undersurface of the jellyfish's umbrella-shaped body.

Incidentally, although there is the temptation to speak of this Medusa (*Aurelia aurita*) as the common jellyfish of the coasts of Britain, the species is world-wide, occurring in all waters from the poles to the equator. Throughout this wide range there is little variation in its structure, although there are probably a number of subspecies capable of breeding at different temperatures and at different seasons of the year. These things have not, however, been fully investigated.

Since the name Medusa was first given to this one particular jellyfish, it has been more widely applied to jellyfish of many kinds and has acquired a particular significance for the group, the Coelenterata, to which jellyfish belong. Medusae, in this broader sense may range in size from those invisible to the naked eye to the largest jellyfish. They belong, however, to different classes of animals, although all belong to the **one phylum, the** Coelenterata.

By contrast with the sponges, the Coelenterata, which rank next in ascending order in the animal scale, show a most unusual diversity of form. Included in it are the familiar jellyfish, the sea-anemone and the stony corals, of reef-building fame. There are also the precious corals, sea-firs, sea-pens and the freshwater hydra. Such a list gives, however, no more than a selection, a few of those that have received common names. They include animals barely visible to the naked eye to those several feet across, from soft-bodied forms consisting of almost 100 per cent of water to the reef-builders, almost 100 per cent of lime-stone, from bladders of gas, such as the Portuguese Man-o'-War, floating on the surface of the sea and trailing their menacing tentacles through the waters beneath, to those habitually burrowing in the mud at the bottom of the sea and trailing their tentacles on the surface thereof. Whatever their form, they all agree in one thing, that they possess stinging cells, the so-called nematocysts, which are as much a trade-mark of the group to which they belong as is the limy shell of the molluscs; more so in fact, since the lamp-shells are not molluscs, although they, too, have a limy shell. But there is virtually no other animal with nematocysts, and for an easy comparison we have to come on land to the nettles, whose stinging cells work on a similar principle.

In spite of their great apparent differences, the ground plan of all the Coelenterata is remarkably similar. Indeed, this group furnishes one of the most striking examples of a wide diversity in appearance springing from minor changes in the ground plan. Or, in other words, they indicate how slight changes in the genes can produce far-reaching alterations in form and in the potentialities for functioning. Moreover, this ground plan or fundamental design is pre-served in spite of a quite characteristic revolutionary change within the span of every generation, known as the alternation of generations. This is best seen, in its simplest form, in the section of the Coelenterata known as the sea-firs. Many of the sea-firs are insignificant and generally pass unnoticed even by those well familiar with the sea-shore. If noticed at all they are probably dismissed as some kind of diminutive seaweed. They are as ubiquitous as seaweeds, and form a fair proportion of the low growths coating the walls of rock-pools or ornamenting the shells of mussels, oysters and other such sedentary marine animals. The larger of them are more familiar to the beach-comber as the drab-coloured feathery objects, up to a foot long, lying cast up on the shore at low tide or mingling with the flotsam and jetsam in the drift-line. These have what appears to be a central stem surrounded by whorls of branches, giving something of the effect of a fir-tree. Probably the more descriptive and apt term is that given by the American biologists, sea-plume.

Hercules' task in killing the monster of Lerna lay in the fact that as soon as he cut off any of the nine heads they were replaced with others. One can but express surprise how often human invention in mythology runs close to a natural actuality, for we may assume that the Ancient Greeks, in concocting their myths, knew little of biology, although later their philosopher Aristotle was so astonishingly right in many of his discoveries despite his lack of scientific apparatus. In any case, it has enabled the biologist of more recent times to draw largely on that mythology in naming the animals since discovered. There is living in the rivers and lakes a freshwater representative of the sea-firs. It has a green cylindrical body, up to an inch long, crowned with a ring of a half-a-dozen tentacles. This has been named Hydra, for it will not only grow a new tentacle in place of one cut off, but if its body is cut in two will form two bodies. The lower half will grow a new crown of tentacles and the upper half a new base. In fact, it can be cut into several pieces and there will be re-grown as many Hydras.

The fact that Hydra is green or brown, and is for the most part stationary, suggests a plant-like quality, although the colour is, to an extent, fortuitous, being due to microscopic plants living within the animal's cells. The ability to re-grow lost or injured parts is also plant-like. If its marine relatives are mistaken for plants there is even

more excuse, for they are made up of polyps each consisting of a cup-shaped body surrounded by a wreath of tentacles at the rim. Sometimes the polyps are borne on single
stalks arising from the substratum, more commonly an
erect branching stem bears a series of polyps at intervals,
or, as in the case of the larger sea-firs, already referred to,
there is a main stem and many branches each of which
branches again to carry numerous polyps. Each polyp is a
single individual connected by a living stem with the main
stock, so that the whole colony, often comprising several
hundred polyps, is one continuous living entity. Or, to
start at the beginning of the story, when the larva first
settles on the surface of a rock, pebble or shell, it grows into a stem bearing a polyp at the top. Then a bud appears
lower on the stem, and this grows out into a second stem
and flowers a polyp at the end. By repeated branching and
flowering the colony is built up. One larva is responsible
for many polyps. This vegetative reproduction as it is
called, an obvious reflection again on the plant-like qualities of the animals, reflects a capacity for growth closely
similar to the budding and fragmentation seen in sponges,
for both these processes are alike in principle.

There is all the difference in the world, so far as appearance is concerned, between the Hydrozoa, or Hydrome-
dusae, as the sea-firs are collectively called and the masses
of reef-building stony corals. Yet the mode of growth is the
same in principle and the so-called coral "insect" of the
earlier writers is a flower-shaped polyp. The name of
the class to which the stony corals, as well as the precious
corals, sea-anemones, sea-pens, sea-fans, and others, are
relegated is the Anthozoa, literally flower-animals. Apart
from the more elaborate tissues, a more complicated anatomy, and usually larger size, there is no essential difference between the polyp of the Hydrozoa and that of the
Anthozoa. In both the body is cup- or sac-shaped, with
a mouth at the apex surrounded by a ring of tentacles.

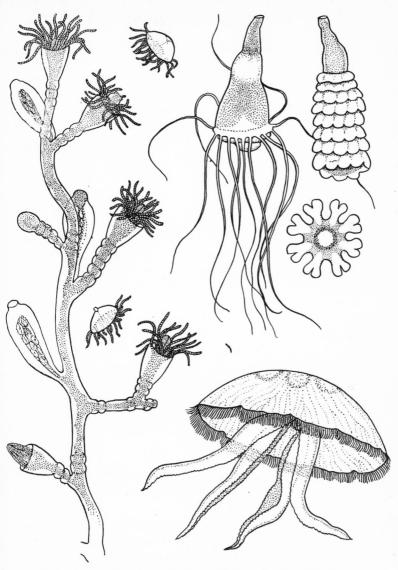

The birth of small and large jellyfishes. Sea-fir on the left and Medusa on the right.

Moreover, in all, the tentacles are armed with batteries of stinging cells and all feed by paralysing whatever is unfortunate enough to come into contact with their tentacles. Naturally, the smaller the polyp the smaller the victim it can overpower, but the generalisation remains good.

In spite of the tremendous potential for multiplication within the colony, the polyps of the sea-firs themselves take no other part in reproduction. At intervals along the stem, in a typical sea-fir, arise vase-shaped receptacles, the wall made of a horny non-living material akin to that coating the bodies of insects, and having at its centre a rod of living tissues. This, again, is able to bud profusely, but instead of budding off polyps which are cup-shaped with a ring of tentacles and remain fixed to a support, it gives off saucer-shaped polyps, with ornamented edges that become detached and float freely out into the sea through the opening at the top of the horny vase. These medusae are in effect minute jellyfish of simple design, and in that simplicity reveal their similarity in form to the polyps. There is, however, one important difference, apart from the fact that the medusa swims upside down as compared with the position normally held by the polyp. It is that the medusa carries germ-cells. These are shed into the sea to give rise, by fertilisation of the ova, to larvae, which later settle on the bottom to grow into fresh colonies of polyps, thus completing the cycle.

This long explanation has been necessary to explain two things: the alternation of generations and the fundamental similarity between the individuals produced in both generations. The polyp-forming colony which we normally recognise as the sea-fir is the hydroid generation. It represents the asexual phase of the life story. The medusoid generation is the sexual phase, and the two generations alternate. This, like the asexual fragmentation and budding of sponges has exercised a profound influence on the evolution of the animal.

To return to the jellyfish with which we started, although it may be a gross over-simplification to express it this way, yet the fact remains that it is no more than a glorified example of the simple medusa of the sea-fir. It is an over-simplification, and yet equally true, to say that it is little more than a glorified sea-fir polyp, turned upside down and free to swim in the sea as a single unit instead of being joined to its fellow. What is more it is the medusoid generation in its own life story. The jellyfish, Medusa, Sea-Wasp, or what it may be, carries ova or sperms, as the case may be, and its larvae settle on the bottom, to grow into something very like the Hydra, or, for that matter a simplified version of a sea-anemone. Moreover, this, the so-called scyphistoma, indulges in budding, on the same principle as that already examined in detail in the sea-fir. Instead of forming polyps, however, the scyphistoma soon begins to look like a pile of saucers, and as time goes on first the top saucer, then the next and so on, become detached from the pile to float away and grow into new jellyfishes.

In addition to the diversity in form between the various members of the Coelenterata, there is a great diversity in structure, which is no more than we should expect. Continuing the simplification, we may summarise the Coelenterata as follows: the Hydrozoa or sea-firs, have two alternating generations, a hydroid and a medusoid generation, the former predominating; the Scyphozoa, the jellyfishes proper, have the same two alternating generations but here it is the medusoid which predominates; and the Anthozoa, the sea-anemones, corals, sea-pens and the rest, there is only one generation, the hydroid, the medusoid having been suppressed. The shapes of the various polyps and medusae are fundamentally the same, and in spite of all their differences are mere variations on a single restricted theme, as much so as might be produced by a milliner with a supply of hat shapes who fashions and decorates each one individually, thereby filling a shop-window with a series of hats no two of which are recognis-ably similar except under a close scrutiny.

The Coelenterata go far back in time, and although medusae had little chance of being preserved as fossils, corals had, and so had the sea-firs, whose stems, branches and polyps are for the most part clothed in a protective sheath of chitin. And from the earliest fossil-bearing rocks there is evidence of their existence. Some groups have died out, others have taken their places; there has been con-stant change, but the evidence available suggests that there is little if any fundamental difference in the structure or the mode of life. For a long span of time, for something like five hundred million years, or more, there has been this variation on a simple theme.

The very simplicity of the theme coupled with its per-sistence suggests a relatively limited number of genes in the Coelenterate chromosomes, and for that matter a rela-tively limited number of chromosomes. Secondly, we get an impression of how the ultra-microscopic genes can alter, radically to all appearances, the shape and structure of their possessors by a number of small permutations and combinations of stalk-length, body-size, tentacle growth and so on. If this be so, however, it is necessary to explain why there has been so little departure from the basic design over this vast period of time. In other words, what is the limiting factor inhibiting progress as we know it in other stocks that have stemmed from the same ancestral form as the Coelenterata? The answer lies in the import-ance of sexual reproduction as a means of mixing the gene material to produce more intricate groupings which in turn influence the formation of fresh structures, themselves the raw material for further evolution.

There is an interesting study here in population potenti-alities, although in the present state of our knowledge the deductions must be from first principles than from concrete evidence. I made the point in dealing with sponges that they have remarkably few enemies. The same seems to be true of the Coelenterates. Some fishes, notably the parrot-fishes, puffers and porcupine fishes break off pieces of coral, bottom feeding fishes sometimes take sea-anemones and we may assume that plankton feeders take medusae of various sorts, especially the smaller kinds, incidentally, if no more. On the other hand, we have the familiar stories of the protective value of the stinging cells of jellyfish and anemones, all of which go to suggest that the Coelenterates are avoided by the majority of marine animals as we avoid a bed of nettles, and for a similar reason.

There is, for instance, the classic example of the hermit-crab living in a whelk shell, with one or more anemones riding on the shell, a partnership so close that when the hermit changes its shell it is said to stroke the anemone and induce it to clamber on to the new band-waggon. It seems reasonable enough to suppose that the crab obtains a measure of protection from its enemies, especially during the vital seconds when it is withdrawing the soft part of its body and transferring it to the new home, and that the anemone gains something from the scraps of food let loose as the crab tears up the carrion it comes across. Then there is the crab that carries a small sea-anemone in each claw, presumably to brandish in the face of a would-be foe, although I would be as soon prepared to believe that it lets them catch food and then robs them of their victims, another version of the cat's-paw technique. As against such interesting and relatively harmless activities must be put the innate destructiveness of crabs, which from my observation seem prepared to tear anything to pieces that comes their way, whether it is palatable or not, and sea-anemones could very well suffer occasionally in this way. Taking it all round, however, there is no attrition among the mature Coelenterates comparable with, say, the depredations among insects by birds, or among shrews, mice and voles by a variety of predatory mammals and raptorial birds. There must be, therefore, an unusually heavy mortality among the broods, which immediately lessens the amount of gene material to be worked on.

On the other hand, sea-anemones, at least, are resilient in the face of other forms of attrition. They are long-lived, or at least some of them are, if we may judge by the now classic instance of the anemone that lived at least 70 years in captivity. They also have the ability, in times of shortage, to diminish in size, filling out again and continuing growth when food is again plentiful. Although they have lost the vegetative generation which forms the main generation in the sea-firs, they have other methods of asexual reproduction. Some anemones will on occasion split in two lengthwise to form two individuals. Other anemones will, as they creep about the rocks, leave portions of their basal disk behind, each piece reforming to grow into a small anemone. We may take it then, that even in the sea-anemones asexual reproduction forms no negligible part of the total means of multiplying numbers in a population.

We should recall that the great advantage of sexual reproduction, from an evolutionary point-of-view, lies in the mixing of gene material from two parents having different genes complexes, making for greater potentialities for combination and re-combination of characters. Thus is presented a greater range of fluctuating variation and of mutation upon which the pressure of natural selection can operate. In asexual reproduction the offspring receives gene material from the single parent, giving the minimum opportunity for change in any new direction. In any species, under normal and stable circumstances, just sufficient of the offspring survive to counteract the wastage by death in the mature individuals of the population. In other words, to maintain the population any two parents must, on an average leave at their death two offspring to survive them. The longer-lived they are the fewer offspring necessary to survive from the aggregate of broods they have produced in order to keep the numbers steady. Although we speak of a natural selection, the term is misleading in one sense, that it is not selective, but random, in so far as the mortality of offspring is concerned. True selection operates only when a mutant having greater potentiality for survival enters into an unstable environment.

Where half the offspring, or any such appreciable proportion, is asexually produced the possibility of change due to mixing of the gene material is significantly reduced. Linked with the other factors we have discussed, such as the stability of the sea as an environment, the probable longevity of the individual, and the small survival rate of the young, asexual reproduction becomes a drag on progress. It is significant that as we ascend the animal scale asexual reproduction increasingly gives place to sexual method. It is also significant that asexual reproduction is rare in land animals. The emergence of sexual reproduction is, therefore, the chief means of determining the evolutionary fortunes of the species. It is a cause and not an effect.

It would be interesting to know whether the littoral species in these lower groups of animals show a higher percentage of sexually produced offspring as against comparable species in the deeper waters. So far as I know there has been no such analysis made on a statistical basis. From direct observation on sponges, my guess would be that this is so and that it is one of the major factors in the invasion of the beaches from the deeper waters.

In Coelenterates, at all events, we have a similar situation to that found in sponges. The dependence upon water is not so great in so far as there is no vital stream circulating through the body, bringing both food and oxygen. There is, however, little power of locomotion. Jellyfishes, in spite of the pulsations of the umbrella do no more than drift with the current, although they may alter their position relative to the current itself. The external form and the internal structure are more stable than in sponges although the animal as a whole retains something of their regenerative powers, and use it in asexual reproduction. Above all there is no internal fertilisation, only the random shedding of ova and sperms into the sea, there to take the chance of accidental meeting.

Although, from all other points of view, the Coelenterates may be taken to show an advance on sponges, their penetration into fresh waters is less spectacular. Sponges are found in considerable numbers, and in a wide variety of species, in all the fresh waters throughout the world, but apart from the Hydras there is but a limited number of medusae, the first of which was discovered in the water lily ponds of the Royal Botanic Gardens in Regent Park in 1880.

Perhaps the most important lesson to be derived from the Coelenterates concerns the factor for constant change. Although living in a relatively stable medium, whereby natural selection is at a minimum, and although the use of asexual reproduction significantly reduces the opportunities for genetical mutation, there has been constant change. This exposes the importance of random mutation in evolution. It is easy to see how, as the pressure of natural selection and the possibilities for genetical change increase, as they do the higher we go in the animal scale, the tempo of evolution will be accelerated.

CHAPTER SEVEN

MYSTERY OF THE SELF-STARTER

BEFORE telling my story I feel bound to explain that the events with which it is concerned took place many years ago, for although they resulted in a discovery they were somewhat flippant in origin. I was watching some sea-anemones in a pool, and enjoying the beauty of their varied colours showing to advantage in the crystal clear water. There was a dead shrimp on the edge of the pool and, mesmerised no doubt by the gently waving tentacles of the anemones, I pulled its carcase to pieces, and dropped a small piece on to one of the tentacles. I had often read of the way an anemone fed and now I wanted to see for myself. As the piece of shrimp settled, the tentacle bearing it started to bend over towards the mouth situated in the middle of the ring of tentacles. As it started slowly to do this, a nearby tentacle also started to move as if in sympathy. Then another began to move, and another, until most of the tentacles were moving, writhing like so many snakes, and all more or less in the direction of the mouth. It is true that the piece of shrimp was larger than the food normally taken by the anemone, but it seemed an unnecessary expenditure of energy that all the tentacles should combine to help. Eventually, however, the piece of food was pushed, rather fumblingly, into the mouth, after which the tentacles started to move outwards again, back into the normal, searching positions.

I had fed several of the anemones in this way, when it occurred to me to wonder what would happen if there were a surfeit of food. Would the animal over-eat or would the tentacles show some degree of co-operation and reject part of the food? What power of selection had the animal as a whole? I pulled the rest of the shrimp carcase to pieces, placing the bits in a row on the edge of the pool. When these unusual rations were lined up, I dropped each piece in turn, the one rapidly following the other, on to each of the tentacles. As soon as the first piece touched the first tentacle it started to move inwards, but before the others could really get going I had dropped all that remained of the shrimp, which meant the greater part of its carcase, bit by bit on to the moving tentacles. The stimulus of the accumulated food caused them to move slightly faster, I thought, but not very much so. And the pattern of the movement was the same as when the single piece was dropped on to one tentacle. In time, however, each tentacle had placed its food in the mouth. It was difficult to follow quite what happened, for the region over the mouth was obscured by a twisting, turning mass of tentacles. Slowly they returned to the normal position, however, after all the fragments of shrimp had been engorged.

There was not long to wait for the sequel. The disk at the top of the anemone's body, the so-called oral disk, with the mouth at the centre and the tentacles springing from its perimeter, began to heave upwards, like a volcanic mountain emerging from the sea in the birth of an oceanic island. At the same time, the mouth began to open, disclosing one end of an agglutinated mass of shrimp. Perhaps the whole procedure for which I had been responsible, was a foolish one. And, indeed, at this distance of time I am almost ashamed to admit to having played this unfair trick on the anemone. The result was, however, quite spectacular. Slowly the oral disk continued to rise and, at the same time, the ring of tentacles as slowly began to migrate towards the base of the anemone. To cut a long story short, one that took perhaps five minutes to be enacted, there arrived the moment when instead of an anemone with its column surrounded at the summit with

a ring of tentacles, there was an anemone with a ring of
tentacles almost at the base of the column and an abnorm-
ally extended oral disk, bullet-shaped and leaning to one
side, slowly disgorging the mass of shrimp-meat. This
done, it sank flaccidly on to the rock, with every appearance of utter exhaustion at the feat accomplished.

The distressing appearance of the anemone in its seemingly exhausted state was such as to cause me prickings of
conscience, but there was nothing I could do except watch
for its recovery. This came in a surprisingly short space of

Snake's-head sea-anemone feeding; the particle of food is
nearing the mouth.

time. After a few minutes, the tissues began to show a return to the normal firmness, the tentacles started to migrate back up the column of the body, and the oral disk
moved back to its normal shape, size and position in the
body. In ten minutes, the anemone was back to normal,
and readily accepted the single piece of shrimp-meat
thrown to it.

It has been impossible to recount this story without the
frequent use of the word "slowly". Yet, for a sea-anemone,
the over-gorging and the rejection of the surfeit of food by
what almost amounted to turning itself inside out, took

place at breakneck speed. It was all done in about a quarter of an hour. Apart from any other consideration, it presented a sea-anemone in a new light. As normally seen, they are comparatively lifeless, except for the gentle waving of the tentacles in search of food. And even this seems aimless. It is true that if touched an anemone will withdraw within itself at a moderately good speed, but under usual conditions this seems the only purposive action of which it is capable. On the other hand, cinematograph films taken of the everyday movements of some species of anemones, and then projected on to a screen at sixty times the speed, reveal them as active creatures displaying movements that appear purposive.

Although the body of a sea-anemone shows a considerable increase in organisation on that of a sponge, or even on that of a hydroid, it is still of the kind that justifies the use of the word "lowly". There is no digestive tube, the digestive cavity being merely the interior of the sac-shaped body, into which a number of digestive tissues hang like a series of curtains. There is only one opening to the exterior, the mouth. There is a good series of muscles; a set of muscles running longitudinally from the foot to the oral disk, and a series of circular muscles, running round the body, and it is by the interplay of these that a peristaltic movement is imparted to the body enabling it to lengthen or retract. There is also a series of retractor muscles. The nervous system is, however, nothing like so highly organised, consisting as it does of a network of nerve-cells, with no well-defined nerves and no central nervous control corresponding to the brain of higher animals. It was at one time assumed that with such a lowly organisation, its behaviour must be largely a matter of response to external stimuli. It was noted that an anemone would withdraw if touched: that it would extend its tentacles on immersion in water; and that these tentacles would bend over towards the mouth if stimulated by contact with food. In other words, that it came very near to being the complete automaton. My own haphazard and rather foolish experiment suggests otherwise, since it was able to cope with an unusual situation by a very unusual behaviour.

The more extensive and precise researches of physiologists since that time have shown beyond question that there is an inherent behaviour in sea-anemones which is rhythmic, independent of external stimuli, and which is, as shown by the speeded cinematograph film, apparently purposive. This is important, for during this same time there has grown up a tendency among zoologists to conceive of the behaviour of the lower animals exclusively in terms of response to external stimuli. And although these later investigations are far from conclusive, they have an importance in correcting our perspective in this matter.

Some of the more important of these researches carried out in this country have been on the anemone known as the plumose anemone. This, cream to orange in colour, may sometimes be found at the lower levels of low-tide, although it grows best just below this, where it is permanently submerged. Its oral disk is surrounded with a mass of closely-set small tentacles having the appearance somewhat of eiderdown. Before describing the results of the investigations made on it, which, incidentally, are too extensive to be considered here except in their salient features, it may be as well to describe some of the categories into which animal behaviour fall.

It was natural that the early work on the genes should have been directed more especially to the transmission of what may best be called structural features, these being the more obvious and the more readily correlated with gene-changes. Changes in structure must clearly influence behaviour. There are, however, in addition to the better known reflexes, well-defined inheritable behaviour patterns, and many of these have been shown to be

independent of the environment in that they will operate
in the absence of stimuli from the outside. Their importance in evolution must be high, but their study is still
somewhat in the early stages.

An example of the influence of structure on behaviour is
seen in Hydra. This has four kinds of nematocysts, three of
which are concerned with the capture of food, but the
fourth, operating at a low intensity, is concerned with a

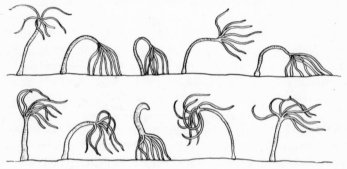

The "cartwheel" in nature: hydra progressing in somersaults.

peculiar form of locomotion. When the tentacles bend over
and touch a solid object, this fourth set of nematocysts,
stimulated by contact, causes the tentacles to become
attached to the surface, the head end to bend over, and
the foot or base to move into a new position. The tentacles
then move to a new position, take hold, the foot is released
to take up a new position. These actions are repeated
alternately in a series of movements known as somersaulting. The contact of the nematocysts sets up a reflex action,
which is communicated to the tentacles, and this in turn
brings into action an inherent behaviour pattern, the
somersaulting.

Purely reflex action can be seen in the action of a
nematocyst when a piece of food touches its trigger and its
poison thread is discharged. The whole thing is automatic

and, at first, confined to the nematocysts. A reflex is, however, seldom isolated. It represents the rapid reaction to an emergency situation, in this case the paralysing of food before it can escape. Usually it is linked with a behaviour pattern, which may be local in its effect, or may be widespread. The local effect is usually short-lived; the widespread usually long-continued and often difficult to distinguish from the next form of behaviour pattern, the inherent behaviour pattern. A behaviour pattern having a local effect only is seen in a number of sea-anemones when touching the oral disk causes them to contract so that the mouth and tentacles are withdrawn to safety. The action is limited and is not followed by any further marked or continuous activity. The long continued and widespread pattern can be illustrated by what takes place in the plumose anemone. If a dilute solution of a food substance, such as one part in a million of mucus from a mussel, is added to the water in an aquarium a series of reactions, expressed in bodily movements, takes place. The oral disk expands, the tentacles extend into the surrounding water, and the anemone gains in height, the whole process taking place over a period of an hour. The anemone may sway slightly so that the disk and the tentacles are bowed first this way, then that way, in a random but clearly purposive manner. The movements are not connected with the actual intake of food, but are purposive in that they constitute a searching or, what has been called, an appetitive movement. The effect is that the tentacles are given an increased chance of coming into contact with any food that may be in the neighbourhood. The sum total of the movements is a good example of a behaviour pattern, which may be defined as a sequence of activities on the part of an organism which are directed to a goal. It is comparable with what takes place when a cat smells a mouse.

One difference between a reflex and a behaviour pattern is that the activities resulting from the former are

normally stereotyped, while those of the latter are variable·
They may vary from one individual to another, or they
may vary in the same individual from one time to another.
The behaviour pattern is also more complex, being often a
co-ordinated sequence of the activities of several muscle
systems, and does not necessarily depend upon any particular class of physiological mechanism. And while it may
be possible, in its more simple form, of analysis into its
final biochemical components its synthesis gives a fluidity
or plasticity that enables the organism to meet its environmental requirements by any means at its disposal.

What may be called the normal state of the plumose
anemone can be described as follows. From a slightly expanded foot or base the cylindrical column stands three or
four inches high surmounted by its ring of feathery tentacles. In an aquarium tank containing several scores of
these anemones, this norm, as we may call it, is seldom
seen at any given moment. The tentacles will be in various
stages of extension or retraction. The column may be
shortened and thickened, or it may be very much shortened, reduced in diameter and thrown into a series of circular wrinkles, or it may be leaning to this side or that.
Sometimes the whole anemone is dilated, the tentacles
withdrawn, giving the appearance of a balloon anchored
to the ground, or it may be so shrunken and retracted that
it forms no more than a button attached to the surface of
the rock. For the most part, the individual anemones will
be static in these positions, but in one or the other may be
seen movements in the tentacles, or a slow waving movement in the column; or a slow wave may be seen passing
down the length of the column. All these changes were
assumed to be due to feeding responses in various stages
of intensity, or reactions to changes in the environment.
In other words, that they were the summation of reflexes
caused by stimuli from the outer world of the anemone.

When the plumose anemone, so placed that the human

observers could watch its movements against a blackened background, was subjected to close and contiunous scrutiny, and its shapes drawn at intervals, it was suspected that the anemone was carrying out a continuous rhythm of movement. It was of the kind I have already noted in the post-larval sponges. By keeping the anemones under conditions of constant temperature, in water free of food materials, undisturbed by vibrations, it was shown that their activities were independent of external circumstances, that they constituted an inherent, continuous and rhythmic activity. The continuous nature was confirmed by attaching fine levers to various parts of individual anemones, the outer ends of which were in contact with slowly revolving drums covered with smoked paper. Throughout the day and night, by this means, the anemone gave a graphical record of its own activities. Further confirmation was obtained by the speeded-up cinematograph film.

The inherent rhythmic pattern can, of course, be interrupted by external stimuli, by the presence of food, contact of food with the tentacles, and adverse stimuli such as a solid body, which might constitute a danger, coming into contact with the column or the disk or the tentacles. On such occasions the movements would not only tend to be speeded up but would become more markedly purposive in manner. The effect of the inherent pattern of behaviour seems to be that the anemone is kept in a constant state of preparedness, carrying out, so to say, a continual rehearsal of the actions needed for feeding, defence, and all the other activities essential to the maintenance of life. The significant thing is, however, that it is self-starting and self-maintaining.

The mechanism stated briefly, is neuro-muscular. The lengthening of the column is brought about when one set of muscles elongates and at the same time the action of those muscles responsible for shortening the column are inhibited. The waves passing down the column, on the other hand, are brought about by complementary action of longitudinal muscles and circular muscles. The action of the muscles themselves is brought about by impulses passing from one nerve-cell to another in a network extending through the body, for the anemone has no nerve-fibres such as we are familiar with in the higher animals. But although there is this primitive nerve network, with no centres of higher control, the total behaviour of the anemone bears comparison, at least superficially, with the more complex behaviour of the higher animals. It is easy to see that the complementary action of sets of muscles, the mutual inhibitory action between sets of muscles and the passing of nervous impulses along a chain of cells could, with a more elaborate system of muscles and nerves and the necessary organs of locomotion, produce the locomotory movements characteristic of higher animals. In other words, at this low level of animal organisation, where a sedentary habit is the norm, the stage is already set, by the inherent behaviour pattern, for independent locomotion to be a normal function, once the necessary organs come into being.

I have said that the sedentary habit is the norm in sea-anemones. That they are capable of a limited locomotion, can, however, be readily demonstrated by collecting sea-anemones and crowding them together in a quiet rock pool or, better still, in an aquarium. In time they will fix themselves by their bases and the usual activities will be seen. After some hours, the crowd will be seen to have dispersed. Doubtless secretions given off into the water, or oxygen deficiency due to over-crowding, will have given the stimulus. Some anemones move by a gliding action of the foot; others carry out somersaulting movements comparable to those of Hydra. Another species glides on its sides, and another blows itself up and, letting go with the foot, floats away.

The inherent activity has not the same pattern nor the

Plumose anemones in varying phases of rhythmic activity.

same mechanism in all members of the Coelenterata. In the jellyfish there is a set of recognisable nerves of simple construction, and the pulsation used in swimming is due to what is called an automatic excitation comparable to a chain reflex, each contraction of the bell engendering internal stimuli which initiate the next contraction. In Hydra, with its very much simpler muscle system as compared with an anemone, the nervous system forms in part a simple network of nerve-cells and in part of scattered nerve-cells. In this last situation, it must be presumed that the scattered nerve-cells may be the pacemakers for a particular activity but that the body cells are also able to pass on nervous impulses. This is coming near to what is found in sponges, of which a few species have true muscle fibre. In recent years a French scientist has demonstrated the presence of simple nerve-cells, but in the majority of sponges there is no evidence that either muscles or nerve-cells are to be found, yet there is an inherent pattern of behaviour, continuous in the larva and the post-larva at least and in both locomotory in effect. And in the regenerating cells that have been dissociated by passing through a fine silk mesh, locomotion as well as an inherent behaviour pattern can be seen within the space of a generalised cell.

The studies of the behaviour of the lower animals, where activity can be seen in its simpler expression, present us with a picture which is at once readily understandable, and at the same time points the way to an appreciation of what is taking place at the higher, more complicated levels of organisation. Arguing from what we believe to take place in sea-anemones and in sponges, as well as in the division of cells, we can postulate different levels of inherent behaviour; or hierarchies of behaviour would perhaps be preferable. The inherent behaviour in the total organism, such as had been exhaustively demonstrated in anemones, can also be expressed as the sum total of an inherent behaviour in each of the organs, such as the tentacles, disk and column. The behaviour of an organism can be expressed as the sum total of the separate behaviour of the constituent tissues, nerves, muscle and the rest. The behaviour of the tissues is the synthesis of that of the component cells. Within each cell, the nucleus expresses its inherent behaviour pattern in the breakdown of the cell wall, the formation of the chromosomes and of the mitotic spindle. By analogy, we may presume the chromosomes to be demonstrating in their movements an inherent behaviour pattern, and there seems no reason why we must stop short at this point. Merely because it has not yet been demonstrated in the obvious and detailed way in which the gross behaviour of a whole organism has been exposed, there is no ground for denying an inherent pattern of activity in the individual genes. Indeed, a continuous rhythmic activity, with varying phases of intensity and capable of modification by response to stimuli, external to the gene itself, seems a *sine qua non* of genetical phenomena.

The behaviour of the individual sea-anemone varies from day to day, it tends to differ from that of its fellows, but these variations are sufficiently limited that we can recognise a typical and relatively stable pattern. In some, on the other hand, the behaviour may be highly individualistic—there are such aberrant individuals in all species and in all groups—and their behaviour shows a marked change from the average behaviour of their fellows. The picture built up of the behaviour of the genes accords very closely with this.

In all animals, there are individuals capable of an extravagant behaviour which is abnormal for the species. It may be behaviour of this kind in the gene which is responsible for gene-mutation. This does not explain either of the abnormalities, but it helps in our appreciation of them.

CHAPTER EIGHT

A LUGWORM'S RHYTHMS

THE lugworm lives between tide-marks on sandy or muddy beaches often in large numbers. As is usual with burrowing animals, we are more familiar with the signs of its activities than with the animal itself, unless we are given to digging it up for bait. It lives in a U-shaped burrow, the base of which is about a foot below the surface. At the surface the two openings are obscured, the one by a pile of cylindrical castings, and the other, a few inches away, by a saucer-shaped depression. Close watch of these two will show the sand occasionally sinking in the saucer and, less often, the pile of cylinders being added to by fresh material given out, like tooth paste from a tube. The worm itself, some eight or nine inches long, shows three well-marked divisions to the body. A short head end, blackish in colour; a reddish middle portion, of nineteen rings bearing bristles in rows along each side, and all but the first six bearing tufts of skin, the gills, and a brownish-yellow, somewhat narrower hind end, without either bristles or gills. The worm normally lies at the base of the burrow, taking in through the mouth sand which lies at the bottom of the shaft going down vertically from the saucer-shaped depression. Hence the periodic sinking of the sand in the saucer. The sand passes through the body and is periodically ejected through the opening at the head of the other vertical shaft of the "U". Periodically also, water is driven through the burrow, in a direction from the tail to the head, by waves of swelling passing along the body.

Many different kinds of ringed-worms, or Annelida, are

to be found between tide-marks. The burrowing bristle-worms have already been noted in a previous chapter. There are also the ragworms, mainly carnivorous, which crawl actively about or swim; the tiny worm that builds a coiled limy tube, looking like a small mollusc shell, commonly seen attached in large numbers to the fronds of sea-weeds; and, finally, the sea-mouse which, by an over-development of the bristles on the back, its flattened shape and habit of creeping has earned it the name of sea-mouse. Among all these, the lugworm, so highly special-ised in form and habit, is chosen here for several reasons. In the first place, considerable research has been carried out on it in recent years, by G. P. Wells, as a result of which its behaviour is known in fair detail. Secondly, what is known now of that behaviour carries us on naturally from the detailed work on the plumose anemone, de-scribed in the last chapter. Thirdly, there is a similarity between the habits of the lugworm and the earthworm that have invaded the land.

The comparison of these two illustrates therefore one line along which a transition from a purely marine life to one on land could take place, although there is no reason to suppose that the transition has been direct. Both live by burrowing, by swallowing quantities of the substratum in which they burrow and throwing their castings on to the surface. Neither moves far from that burrow, but whereas the lugworm leaves its burrow at breeding time to shed its germ-cells in the sea for random fertilisation, earthworms, although hermaphrodite, use an internal fertilisation with a coupling of two individuals. Earthworms satisfy the minimum requirements, therefore, for life in a non-aquatic medium, namely, internal fertilisation, a limited power of locomotion, and an ability to survive the absence of water in bulk. They do, however, readily suffer desicca-tion and are bound to a moist environment, except for limited excursions on the surface.

In passing, it may be noted that the Annelida are divisible into three groups. The bristle-worms, including the lugworm, are entirely marine; although some can tolerate brackish water. The earthworms and their relatives, forming the second group, with fewer bristles than the marine forms, but otherwise having much in common with them structurally, are found in fresh water but more especially in damp soil. And, finally, there are the leeches, again found in fresh water or in damp situations. All agree in having the body divided into a number of rings or segments, and moving about, either swimming or crawling, by the use of rhythmic waves passing along the body. These are possible because of their complex muscle system, complex, that is, as compared with that of the most muscular of the Coelenterates. And their possession of this is due to a simple but significant change in the organisation of the tissues.

In the early developmental stages of the individual in the higher animals, including man, the early divisions of the fertilised ovum are followed by what is known as the formation of a gastrula. That is a rounded body composed of two layers of cells, an inner endoderm and an outer ectoderm. This corresponds in its architecture with the body of most of the Coelenterates, especially of the sea-firs. In them, each polyp is two-layered. There is in many of them no more than a hint of muscle cells and, as we have seen, there is in many no more than a simple nervous system of scattered cells. In others, like the sea-anemones, the nervous system has become somewhat more co-ordinated, large muscle-fibres have been developed, but the digestive system is still simple. Feeding consists of taking the food through the mouth into a capacious sac, forming the interior of the body, where the food is digested. The indigestible residue, the waste, must, however, be ejected through the mouth. There may be slight elaborations on this simple ground plan, as in the sea-anemones and corals, in which the endoderm is folded to form the so-called mesenteries, hanging down like a series of curtains into the digestive cavity, and thereby increasing the area of the digestive surface. In essence, however, the structure is that of a simple sac, with a single opening, the whole bounded by what is essentially a two-layered wall. The very simplicity of this design imposes severe limitations on any further elaboration of the body. The appearance of an elaborate nervous system is unnecessary for the work to be performed, and would be a disadvantage, since it would give what is in effect an over-powered motor. Excessive development of muscle would be a disadvantage because of the difficulty of supplying the muscle with food except by some system of food-carrying vessels corresponding to our arteries and veins. Another decisive change was necessary for further improvements to be made. This came in the change from a two-layered to a three-layered plan.

From all the evidence available, this is what appears to have taken place. A third layer of tissue appeared at an early stage in the development. Briefly, this made available the cells which, by their subdivision gave the materials for the elaboration of a more complex muscle system. Also, by splitting to enclose a cavity, the body cavity or coelom, gave the needed space within the bounding walls of the ectoderm at the exterior and the endoderm at the interior, for the digestive organs, excretory organs, and other structures such as the lungs, to be contained. Although lungs are not used by marine animals, the usual form of gill-respiration being sufficient so long as the animal is bathed in a fluid in which oxygen is dissolved, the presence of this body cavity made the way for lungs to develop. Without such a cavity and without lungs, or some other substitute, such as the tube-system (tracheal) of insects, emergence on land, except in the limited way seen in earthworms, would have been impossible.

The Annelida have this three-layered design. They are not the most primitive of three-layered animals. There is a whole series of other forms, extremely unfamiliar animals for the most part even to students of biology. And these, if they do not represent the line of evolution from the two-layered Coelenterate to the three-layered Annelid, at least suggest how, once the three-layered design had been established, progress could have been made.

Once a breach has been made in a dyke the water can flood through, and it seems that evolution often has this character. A striking example, observed in recent times, is given in chapter 13. We may suppose then, that once the three-layered stage in animal evolution had been reached the way lay open, by further mutations, for the rapid development of the more complex muscle system, the higher nervous system to control the muscles, more efficient feeding to keep the muscles at work, better methods of excretion to clear away the by-products, and with the muscles to activate them, special organs of locomotion. This is a brief, and somewhat inadequate account of the possible changes that took place, a very long time ago, and certainly before the beginning of the Cambrian period, and it is fully expounded in the many books on evolutionary biology. The synopsis is given here for two reasons. First, to emphasise that this change, relatively simple in itself, merely by the addition of a third layer of tissue in the developing embryo, was a decisive step in what was to follow. And, secondly, to point out, by recalling what we know of the inherent behaviour patterns of the plumose anemone, that the mechanism for using the structures allowed by this third layer was already in being. In other words, with slight modifications, although, of course, with further elaborations of them, the behaviour patterns seen in the two-layered animals were already available for use by the three-layered organisms that succeeded them. This will be more clear as we examine what is known of the behaviour of the lugworms, and, later, of the starfish.

The lugworm is particularly appropriate for the study of an inherent behaviour. To begin with, living more or less permanently in a burrow it is subject to a relatively constant environment. This is axiomatic. The same is true of all burrowing animals, and among other things explains the continued existence in deserts of animals which, physiologically, are not suited to that habitat. Even an inch or two under the soil, the temperature varies little through the day although it may move from intense heat to a bitter cold from day to night at the surface. The effects of evaporation are less felt, whether by a desert animal or an inter-tidal animal. Moreover, although waves may lift the

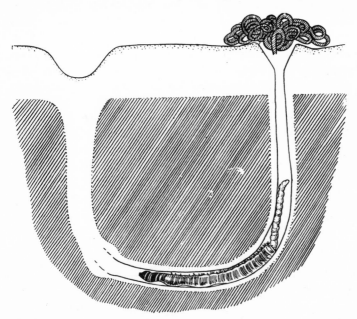

Lugworm in its burrow, showing the saucer-shaped depression due to an intake of sand and (right) the familiar pile of castings.

sand to scour surface animals, its effect on burrowing animals is negligible since the sand is disturbed to a depth of 1 cm. only per foot of wave-height. This gives a freedom from vibration, from buffeting or, on the shore, swirl and scour. In the lugworm, therefore, there is the opportunity to study an animal receiving a minimum of stimulus from the exterior. If therefore it habitually shows intense activity, it should follow that this springs from within the organism itself and is not, except in very small part, a response to circumstances without. That, indeed, is what was found.

The activities of the lugworm consist of bursts of rhythmic movement followed by periods of rest, the rhythmic outbursts being continuous. The behaviour pattern is, therefore, described as one of activity cycles. Each cycle consists of several phases, associated with feeding, irrigation of the burrow for respiration, and defaecation. The front end of the lugworm's food canal consists of a proboscis which leads into a gullet, and thence into the stomach. Feeding is carried out by everting the proboscis to take in sand, in periods of rhythmic contraction alternating with periods of rest, the whole cycle occupying about seven minutes. The irrigation is carried out in three phases; the worm creeps backwards, to bring the hind end of its body near to the exit of the burrow, where the cylinders of extruded matter are given out. This is followed by forward wave-movement of the gills, producing irrigation, and, usually, by a less strong third phase of tailward irrigation. The irrigation phase takes place about every 40 minutes.

This activity cycle can be compared with the swimming and crawling activities of higher animals. And since these may be due to reflex action or may be spontaneously produced, the question to be settled was to which of these categories the movements in the lugworm belong. The first examination showed that if the head end is severed from the rest of the body and suspended in sea-water, a series of gentle waves continues to flow through the gullet and with each wave the proboscis gives a rhythmic outburst. If then the gullet is severed from the proboscis, the waves continue in the wall of the gullet but cease in the proboscis. In other words, the gullet is driving the proboscis, and since the waves continue in the gullet when it is separated from the rest of the body, the force driving the waves in the gullet must be in its own wall. The supposition is that the driving force is a pacemaker located in the nerves of that wall.

Our refrigerator behaves something like a lugworm. It has a cyclic activity. It has long periods of rest, followed, at fairly regular intervals by short outbursts of activity, which are continuous once the outburst starts. There is also a pacemaker, a thermostatic control which, when the temperature falls below a certain point switches on the motor of the refrigerator to initiate another of those short outbursts of activity. What, then, actuates the rhythms in the gullet of a lugworm? What is this pacemaker? Since feeding is involved, one would suspect a hunger-reflex was setting off the pacemaker. Since, however, the rhythm continues in a piece of gullet, isolated from every other part of the body, including the rest of the digestive tube, the action of the pacemaker must be spontaneous.

Similarly, it might be suspected that the irrigation cycle could be due to the oxygen in the burrow being used up and that the accumulation of carbon dioxide was touching off a reflex. A lugworm kept in a glass U-tube, with a limited amount of water, and no replenishment available, continued the normal irrigation cycle even when there was every reason to believe that it must be suffering from a shortage of oxygen. When, however, a supply of fresh water was made available to it, it irrigated continuously and vigorously for some 40 minutes, and after this, for a short while, the frequency of the cycle was increased. This behaviour recalls that of the heart of a vertebrate, which is known to be controlled by a pacemaker. Again, the defaecation phase of the cycle might be due to the hinder end of the gut being filled with matter for ejection. It was found under test that even when a lugworm was starved, so that the gut was empty, the irrigation cycle, including the defaecation phase, was maintained as under normal conditions.

Cyclic activity is not confined to lugworms. It is found in varying forms at different levels of the animal scale, and, indeed, must enter into the behaviour of almost every animal in the upper parts of the scale. In marine animals, especially those living between tide-marks, there is a tidal rhythm. In others, especially in the surface waters, there is a daily rhythm. Similar rhythms, not so well marked are found in many other bristle-worms, although they have not been so thoroughly investigated as those of the lugworm. Apart, therefore, from the fact that Wells' investigations indicate the existence of this highly interesting rhythmic activity, and that it is an inherent rhythm, there is some point in speculating on what advantage it can be to the lugworm.

The littoral zone is, as we have earlier postulated, a zone of rigorous physical conditions. It has also been pointed out that the burrowing life of the lugworm shelters it from the normal rigours. On the other hand, the flat beaches the worm inhabits are often covered at low tide with puddles or sheets of water which in summer can heat up appreciably during the hours that elapse before the return of the tide. Equally, in winter these residual waters can be very cold; or a heavy downpour can cover the beach with a layer of fresh water, or at least water of a very low salinity. If during any such period, the normal irrigation cycle resulted in drawing into the burrow a quantity of water warmer, colder or less salt than normal the result could be very damaging.

According to another investigator, lugworms can live for days in water containing very little oxygen and, at the same time, heavily charged with sulphuretted hydrogen. It has also been shown that the haemoglobin in their blood will hold sufficient oxygen to maintain the animal at a high rate of activity for a full hour, without any further supply being available to them. Since, under conditions of oxygen starvation their activity becomes very much reduced, this blood storage would suffice to maintain life under severely adverse conditions for considerably longer than the hour. And, added to this, the muscles also contain haemoglobin. It has been suggested that the cyclic activity provides a device by which the external conditions can be periodically tested. That when the tide is out, the backward phase in the irrigation cycle constitutes a means whereby a watch is kept, as it were, on the state of the tide, so that when the beach is once again covered with water, a full measure of respiratory activity may be resumed to replenish oxygen used up during the time that the beach has been uncovered.

Speculations of this sort are interesting, but they remain speculations. They serve, however, to illustrate the various ways in which structural and physiological changes can enable an animal to occupy a specialised ecological niche. In this particular instance, they illustrate some of the minor rigours of the shore which the animals living there must meet and overcome. Above all, we have a picture of inherent activities, of different kinds and at different levels of organisation, within the body of even the lower animals. Instead of looking at these lower organisms as passive victims of circumstances, we see them possessed of a dynamic which enables them to choose, if only to a limited degree, between favourable and unfavourable conditions, to take advantage of the first and to seek to avoid the second.

CHAPTER NINE

STARFISH AUTOMATA

THE starfish is inseparably linked in the mind with the sea-shore. No picture, whether cartoon, advertisement or decorative drawing of the seaside is complete without at least its one starfish tucked away in the corner. Often it is the only sign of life, except for the human subjects, shown in the picture. Yet it is only an occasional wanderer on to the shore, and no more a regular inhabitant than I am a lawyer because I occasionally stroll into the public gallery of a law court and sit there quietly for a few hours. The real home of starfish is in the off-shore waters, where a sweep with the trawl will often cut through a starfish community and bring them up by the score. But if not truly littoral, it comes very appropriately into our book for several reasons. In the first place, it belongs to the next group in ascending order, and together with the sea-urchins, brittle stars, sea-cucumbers and sea-lilies forms the aberrant phylum of Echinoderms, or spiny-skinned animals. Secondly, it differs from the other forms we have been considering in one striking particular, in being able to move freely about. Moreover, the mechanics of its locomotion have been extensively and minutely investigated.

If you turn a starfish on its back the first thing to happen is that the hundreds of tube-feet lining the grooves running down the underside of each arm begin to wave about in an erratic manner. Their movements are, however, not so disorderly as they appear. There is a general tendency for those to one side of the groove to reach over to that side, and for those on the other side of the groove to grope towards the opposite side. Then the arms as a whole start to

twist and writhe, and sooner or later, some part of one of
the arms will twist far enough to allow one or more of the
tube feet to touch the sand on which the starfish is lying.
As soon as this happens, a change takes place. As the first
tube-feet secure a hold on the ground, those nearest them
turn towards them. The first feet having taken hold, they
retract, pulling that part of the arm nearer to the sand,
enabling the adjacent feet, in turn, to secure a hold, and
the wave gradually passes along the arm, which twists
more and more to one side until finally the starfish per-
forms a somersault and is back in its correct position. Then
it starts to move off, one arm taking the lead and the rest
co-operating with it to move the whole body in one direction. There may be a certain amount of indecisive movement, as though the starfish were making up its mind
where to go, but sooner or later the one direction is decided upon and the starfish moves off.

There is nothing intelligent in these actions, and although the total effect is purposive, in that it achieves an
end beneficial to the organism as a whole, it can be shown
to derive from a synthesis of neuro-muscular reflexes, each
simple in itself and an automatic reaction to a particular
stimulus. To understand this fully, we must start at the
beginning and see how a single tube-foot works. The name,
tube-foot is, perhaps, misleading: it is a cylindrical tube,
ending below in a disk, the whole looking somewhat like
an elephant's leg and moving like one. Above, the tube
ends in a small bladder set within the arm. The wall of the
tube contains a pair of longitudinal muscles. The bladder
is expanded and contracted by a pair of vertical muscle
loops. The tube and the bladder are filled with fluid.
When the muscles in the bladder contract the size of the
bladder is reduced, fluid flows into the foot, which is then
forced out, or protruded. When this same pair of muscles
is relaxed, fluid flows back into the bladder and the foot is
retracted. The muscles in the tube itself co-operate to

assist the action. If the foot is in contact with a solid surface at the moment of retraction, its disk automatically acts as a sucker.

Walking is effected by a reciprocal action in a ring of longitudinal muscles in the upper part of the wall of the tube. If the foot is to be pointed, say, to the north, then the muscle in that ring nearest the north will contract and the muscle to the south will relax. This reciprocal action on the part of opposing muscle fibres gives a simple movement in any direction. The actual step taken is in four stages. The retracted foot is pointed in the direction of movement. It is elongated to touch the ground, its upper end levers forward, the foot is retracted, swung forward again, and the process repeated. In short, it is the same as any other leg movement.

Pedicellaria of a starfish, armed with triple jaws.

The description of the structure and mode of working of the tube-foot is not included here merely to make things more difficult. There is no need to do that with a starfish, the difficulty is already there. The animal with its thousand tube-feet, each capable of independent action, its five arms each capable of moving in a different direction, not to mention the thousands of spines and pedicellariae, minute sets of pincers mounted on movable stalks, ornamenting the skin, each again able to take autonomous action, present a situation far more complex than that of the Old Woman who Lived in a Shoe trying to control her numerous children. The dominant problem in the economy of the starfish is the control of innumerable individual and potentially unruly

members, and this, in itself, presents us with an illuminating facet of the evolutionary story.

The Echinoderms, including the starfish and its relatives, are the only group of animals, apart from the lamp-
shells, that are abundantly found in the seas, almost from
the beginning of time and yet have failed to colonise
either the brackish or fresh waters, or the land. The reason
usually given is that the water-vascular system necessary
to the functioning of the tube-feet ties them inevitably to
the sea. Nevertheless, sponges, which depend upon a constant flow of water through the body, analogous to that
needed by a starfish, have freely invaded all the fresh
waters of the globe. Another explanation is that the respiratory system which consists of tufts of skin protruding as
gills all over the surface could not be accommodated to
fresh water. This again is not a valid reason. All manner of
animals, including notably the fishes, have successfully
made their way up the rivers, using a system of gills not
unlike these in principle. It seems to me that the reason
for the Echinoderm failure to leave the sea arises from
entirely different causes. The same causes, in fact, that
have made this group of animals to diverge so markedly
from the main stream of evolution; has caused them,
indeed, to enter an evolutionary backwater and stay
there.

To return to the tube-feet, each of the muscles mentioned in the description of their functioning requires a set
of nerve-cells, mutually inhibitory in turn, to control the
movements of each of the tube-feet. This together with
the need for similar elements in the nervous control of the
many other members already enumerated, has resulted in
a system of control that has in turn converted the starfish
into the nearest thing to a mechanical robot possible in a
living organism. The animal is said to have no discernible
inherent behaviour pattern. If it has one it must be of a
very low order. Its nervous and muscular mechanism is

primarily designed to react to external stimuli. And to express the situation in neo-vitalistic terms, its directiveness is obscured by the dominance of actions that are purely reflex.

Any account given here of the nervous or muscular systems of the starfish is much simplified. To that extent it cannot be fully adequate, and may at times be slightly inaccurate in detail, though I hope not in principle. It is based largely on the researches of Professor J. E. Smith, whose detailed writings can be readily consulted for amplification of this abbreviated account.

A diagram of the nervous connections actuating a single tube-foot, as Professor Smith has shown, has somewhat the appearance of a diagram of the wiring of a radio-set. Any attempt to expose pictorially or verbally the whole neuro-muscular system would, therefore, be almost comparable to trying to set down in a single diagram the wiring of the whole telephone system of Great Britain, including the details of every hand-manipulated switch-board and every automatic exchange. The starfish's mechanism for control of its unruly members shows that it has solved its problem in the same way as Britain has solved the problem of her numerous unruly members. To expound this two similes may be used.

To begin with the nervous system of a starfish can be grouped into three main sections. First there is a peripheral network of nerve-cells lying in the skin. Although capable of independent functioning, this is also in communication with a system of simple nerve-tracts, lying deeper in the skin, the fibres of which run transversally round the arms, from the mid-dorsal line to the under-surface. There, after giving off single nerve-threads to each of the muscles of each tube-foot, they join the main nerve-cord running along each arm. The five main nerve-cords, one running the length of each of the five arms, join with a nerve-ring running round the inside of the central disk of the body. These three systems may be suitably compared with our method of governmental control: the borough or local council, the county council and the central or national government. In each case, we have these three systems of control, each capable of independent action, the first being under certain circumstances subordinate to the second, and both subordinate to the third, the whole integrated for the welfare of the complete organism, whether starfish or Great Britain.

The second comparison may be made with the telephone system. In that we have local calls, toll calls and trunk calls, corresponding to the peripherical network, the transverse fibres and the main nerves. Through the telephone system human activities can be set in motion or controlled, as the case may be, on a local, regional or national scale. We may even include in our comparison the differences between the hand-operated, or manual, exchanges and the automatic exchanges, comparable in the starfish system with nervous centres of slow and rapid response. To a varying degree, this comparison with a telephone system can be made for all animals. What makes it the more apt in relation to the starfish, and presumably any other of the Echinoderms, is that a telephone system is a purely mechanical organisation, with little or no inherent rhythm of activity.

Let us see how this works in the everyday life of the starfish. To begin with the animal is not particularly active or fast moving. Although capable of locomotion, it is largely static. It could, therefore, readily become covered with barnacles, worm-tubes and all the other things that develop from a free-swimming larva settling on the bottom. Crabs often have such things encrusting their backs, but with them it matters little since they periodically moult their outer shell. The starfish is endowed with pedicellariae disposed over the surface of the body. Anything falling on that surface causes a reflex in the peripheral nervous network, but the impulse does not travel far in it, merely sufficient to bring into action the nearest pedicellaria, which bends over and crushes whatever has touched the surface lightly. It would obviously be uneconomic for all the pedicellariae to be brought into action, over the whole surface, merely because one barnacle larva settled. There is, therefore, an advantage in this method of localised control.

When the surface of the starfish is prodded, say with a pointed probe, however, the greater intensity of its pressure results in an impulse travelling not only through a greater amount of the peripheral net but also down the nearest transverse fibre to the tube-foot directly underneath, causing it momentarily to retract and later to protrude and bend over the side of the groove in which it normally rests. If the pressure is of high intensity, however, it will remain retracted. At the same time, impulses are conveyed to the higher levels of control, the radial nerves and the nerve-ring, which set the tube-feet elsewhere in motion, or if already in motion it accelerates this. The value of these reactions lies in this. Near the point at which the pressure is applied, the tube-foot is withdrawn, protecting it from a possibly harmful visitation. Then follows the impulse causing it slowly to protrude. This supplies the means of testing what is taking place. Since the reaction is the same whether a pressure or a chemical stimulus is applied, this precautionary behaviour of the foot allows for most eventualities. When the intensity of the stimulus, pressure or chemical, is high and is communicated to tube-feet away from the area affected, it results in a total escape movement, a moving away from a source of possible danger.

We can see another value to this reaction. If we imagine a starfish moving over a rock surface, at any given moment a fair proportion of its thousand tube-feet will be in contact with that surface. A sudden wave movement over its back will impart a high intensity stimulus to the whole of the peripheral nervous system. This, conveyed through the transverse nerves, will cause all the tube-feet to retract. Those in contact with the surface will, in retracting, produce suction under the disks, causing them to adhere to the rock surface. By a purely reflex action, therefore, the movement of a wave causes a starfish to hold on, thus avoiding being washed away, or battered on the rocks.

These examples form but a sample to indicate the general working of the three levels of nervous control. To go further than this would be impossible within the limited space available here, but it is clearly along such lines that the majority of the movements of a starfish can be followed. Likewise there is not the space to go into all the permutations and combinations of adverse or favourable stimuli and the way they stimulate the various levels of control; even if they were all known. So we will pass to the movements of the animal as a whole. Even here we are limited by the amount already worked out. Indeed, in all biological research, it takes so long to elucidate and confirm by further tests even one of the actions in the everyday life of a single animal that the best we have is no more than a series of cameos. From these we are obliged to complete the picture largely in the imagination. The obvious thing, of course, once the searching analysis of the laboratory is concluded, is to make close observation of the animal under natural conditions, or, in the case of a marine animal, in an aquarium. The difficulty then arises that when we see the animal do this or that, we are never sure which of the many things happening all the time around it is responsible for this single action. If I see a man running along the street, and have to say why he is running, I might give it as my opinion that he had a train to catch, or that he was hungry and was hurrying home for a meal, or that there was a policeman around the corner seeking to arrest him There might be a score of different reasons why he is running. Fortunately, with a man, one can, if curiosity is sufficiently aroused, go and ask him why he is running. Then we should probably find out that the real reason was none of those we had suspected, but that he was running merely because he had a fancy to do so. With inarticulate animals, we have no such ready means of satisfying curiosity, and we are forced to the laborious method of testing, observing and guessing, with always the

A starfish reacts towards light: the sensitive tube-foot is extended.

prospect that the guess may be wrong. The alternative is to observe their behaviour under strictly controlled and limited laboratory conditions, with the possibility that things do not necessarily go like this in real life.

Let us start with the starfish moving across the shore. We may ask several questions: Where is it going? What is its objective? What makes one arm take the lead rather than one of the other four? Naturally, one arm must take the lead or it would either remain stationary or go round in circles. And is it always the same arm that takes the lead? At the end of each arm there is a tube-foot which is incapable of contraction and is used as a sense-tentacle, or feeler. Above each of these is an eye-spot. So a starfish can react to light. This should be easy enough to put to the test. In fact, if a starfish is turned upside down and a strong beam of light shone on to it from one side, the tube-feet of the arm nearest to the source of light become more active than those on the arms furthest away from the beam. When the animal is the right way up, and free to move, it would therefore travel towards the light. The movement is not as regular and certain as all this, however, for at times one or other of the arms furthest from the source of light can take on a temporary dominance, leading to a certain amount of erratic movement. This grows less as the intensity of light grows greater; that is, the approach will be the more certain as it approaches more nearly the source of light.

A certain way to stimulate a starfish to active locomotion is to introduce a trace of meat extract into the water. The effect is similar to that of a beam of light. The "scent" is picked up by the arm nearest to the source of the extract, and this will give that arm the dominance, initiating a movement towards the source of the extract. The fact that a temporary dominance may be shown by one or other of the arms, suggests that the perception of a possible meal is likely to be accompanied at first by something in the nature of a searching movement, and that as the trail is the more certainly picked up this resolves itself into a purposive and direct approach to the source of food.

If one arm of a starfish becomes accidentally severed, it will move in the direction of the injured end. On the face of it this looks like an attempt to go back to the place where it belongs. The scientific explanation given us is, however, that over-stimulation of the arm, especially adverse stimulation, causes that arm to adopt an attitude of drag. So long as it is still attached this would ensure that the other arms were given the dominance, and the whole organism would move out of danger, as for example if the presence of an enemy were sensed. When the arm is severed it still carries out the activity normal under conditions of shock, but these are now without purpose.

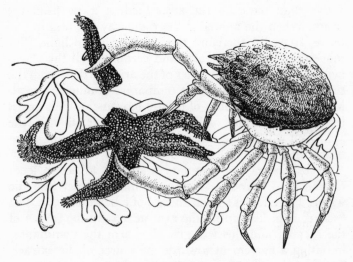

Spider crab feeding on starfish.

Even although the evidence is incomplete, it is sufficient to give us a picture of an animal which has specialised in the use of reflex responses, and to that extent has restricted its chances of undergoing further adaptation. It is, as it were, in an evolutionary rut.

Unfortunately, these exact studies of the behaviour of starfish have not progressed beyond the initial stages, and every step has involved an enormous amount of detailed work. It is not possible, therefore, to apply the lessons learned from them except in a restricted degree. It does look, however, as if the more markedly reflex nature of the behaviour of starfishes, and of the brittle-stars, sea-urchins, sea-cucumbers, and others related to them, has denied them those qualities of adaptiveness and "enterprise" which have carried other animals further along the evolutionary line and also beyond the margins of the sea. Even so, it is still a puzzle why some of them should not have invaded at least the lower reaches of the rivers. All except the sea-lilies have the power of locomotion; there is a differentiation into separate sexes, not very marked, it is true, and a rudimentary form of pairing but without internal fertilisation. But although the reasons for their failure to invade even the freshwaters must be left for future investigators, it is worth remarking that a probable line of descent, as we shall see later, of the more successful vertebrates, may have been from an ancestral stock of the Echinoderms.

It would be misleading to lay such stress on the marked reflex behaviour in starfishes without presenting another side of the picture, as illustrated by the reproductive behaviour of some of the species. The regenerative powers of starfishes are probably as well known as any marine phenomenon. Starfish can regenerate lost arms, and in some species at least an arm can be severed again and again, to be as constantly renewed. Further, if an arm torn away from the body retains even a part of the central disk, it will grow into a complete starfish. These things suggest that, as in sponges and sea-anemones, there must be something in the nature of an inherent rhythm. Even more so is it suggested in those species in which the arms, instead of acting in concert will, on occasion, combine to tear the starfish in halves, by two of the arms moving in the opposite direction to the other three. In an earlier chapter I compared the division of the cytoplasm in Amoeba to the breaking in two of a piece of dough. This was for the sake of brevity. In fact, the division of the cytoplasm there is brought about by the Amoeba throwing out pseudopodia, or false feet, in opposite directions. The process is so remarkably similar in appearance to a starfish tearing itself in half that one suspects an even deeper similarity, and that both will ultimately be traced to an inherent cycle of activity, probably of a very low order.

CHAPTER TEN

RIDDLE OF THE BARNACLE

THOMAS Henry Withers, who made a life-long study of the fossil barnacles, remarked that "The present day may be truly regarded as the Age of Cirripedes, for they occur in countless millions on the shore-line of almost every coast, and are found attached to almost all floating objects and to objects on the sea-bottom." I once made an estimate of the number of acorn barnacles on a mile-stretch of the Sussex coast. Representative areas, each a yard square, were marked off at different points up and down the beach, at low tide, and the barnacles within each area counted. Multiplying the number of these areas to give the total area of the mile of beach, and multiplying again by the average number of barnacles per square yard, I arrived at the total of 2,000,000,000. Sandy and pebble beaches would naturally bear fewer barnacles per mile, but rocky shores would carry many more. The figure may therefore be taken as a fair average of the shore-line populations of barnacles per mile for the British Isles, and possibly throughout the world.

Once figures get beyond a certain point, namely, when they reach the proportions we characterise as astronomical, they cease to have a meaning. Perhaps a more telling way of illustrating the point is to try scrambling hurriedly over the rocks with bare feet, hands and knees. The resulting lacerations of the skin are a sufficient testimony to the ubiquity and the numbers of barnacles. The nuisance value of barnacles goes far beyond such temporary inconveniences, however, for their settlement in large numbers on any bare surface exposed for any length of time to the sea has led directly to major problems. The fouling of ship's bottoms has influenced the course of vital naval actions, slowed up the delivery of merchandise, and caused the expenditure of countless man-hours and currency of many nations in unproductive work. So although the barnacle has never invaded the land it has made its effect felt in the affairs of man, the dominating land animal. The drag on a ship with its hull fouled by them and other organisms associated with them has caused a severe wastage of fuel in an effort to maintain an economic speed. The constant need for periodic dry-docking and the scraping and repainting has diverted a large labour force that could be more profitably employed. And these two things combined has added to the prices of goods so that even in our economics and politics having no obvious connexion with the sea, the sinister hand of the barnacle can still be seen. One consequence is that in recent years there has sprung up a tremendous and widespread research into the life of the barnacle having one end, the discovery of anti-fouling methods. There has arisen, incidentally, a well-established industry for the manufacture of anti-fouling paints. Altogether, there has resulted a place in marine biological research for the barnacle unrivalled by any other single group of animals, with the possible exception of food-fishes.

It is tempting to go further into what is a vital and fascinating problem, but for our present purpose another aspect of the barnacle is the more compelling: that it affords valuable material for the study of at least one aspect of the general story of evolution. To appreciate this fully, we must go back 150 years, to the time when barnacles, with their bodies enclosed in calcareous, shell-like plates, were classified with the Mollusca. This seemed reasonable enough, and even to-day the non-biologist, judging purely from its outward appearance must wonder why it should be otherwise. In 1829, however, J. Vaughan

Thompson worked out the life history of the barnacle. He found that from the egg was hatched a larva that swam freely in the sea. In form this larva differed in minor details only from the larvae of other crustacea, such as crabs and the rest. It was of the type known as a nauplius. After swimming at the surface of the sea for some time, the nauplius changed its shape. It also grew a pair of shells, which encased the body almost completely. It had, in

addition, six pairs of swimming legs and, on the head, a pair of antennae ending in suckers. At this second stage, the larva held a strong likeness to certain other kinds of crustacea, known as the Ostracods, abundant in both the sea and the fresh waters, the latter being known as water-fleas. This second stage of the larval history is known as the cypris. There are, therefore, two strong indications that the true relationships of the barnacles, or Cirripedes as they are known scientifically, are with the Crustacea and not with the Mollusca.

At the end of the larval life, the cypris seeks out a surface upon which to settle. When suited, it turns on to its head, attaching itself by the suckers on the ends of the antennae, throws off the larval shells and assumes the form of the adult, which may be stalked or sessile, or one or the other of the less familiar forms that cirripedes are known to assume. Before considering these several forms, a word is perhaps necessary about the phraseology used in the opening sentence to this paragraph. In that the larval barnacle was described as "seeking out" a place upon which to settle; and attaching itself when suited. As we

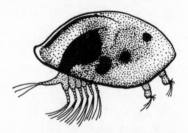

Cypris larva of a barnacle.

have already seen, the strong tendency to-day is to eschew, in describing the behaviour of animals, all words and terms applicable to or reminiscent of human behaviour, and especially those suggestive of a volition. There has been, in other terms a violent reaction to anthropomorphism, the crediting of animals with human emotions and other capacities, especially those connoting a mental capacity. The reaction is a natural one, stimulated largely by the sentimental writings of the latter half of the nineteenth and the early part of the twentieth century. As usual the pendulum has swung too far. It is of interest then to digress at this point and see how far the use of the words "select" and "suited" are justified in speaking of the behaviour of barnacle larvae.

As I have already said, the search for anti-fouling methods has stimulated a considerable research into the lives of barnacles, including the behaviour of the larvae and the conditions under which they settle or fail to settle on a given surface. For example, if it could be determined what surfaces or what conditions of the surfaces inhibited their settlement, then the investigators might be led to a preparation, such as a paint, or a type of surface, which could be applied to a ship's hull and so prevent fouling. This in turn has led to a close observation of the habits and idiosyncrasies of the larvae themselves to the point where the human investigators have almost learned to know the individual larvae by name. And if that is taking things too far, at the least we can say that they have more than a nodding acquaintance with them.

Now there is no doubt that a larva, in the course of settling, is influenced by a number of factors. Some of these can be attributed to an innate behaviour pattern and others can be ascribed to stimuli from the external environment. These can be analysed into their components, but the synthesis of them can only be expressed by saying that a larva is seeking and selecting a place for settlement. We find workers in other fields, independently making the same remarks, as, for example, those who work intensively with the larvae of marine worms.

If we start from the beginning, we find the barnacle larvae, when first hatched, swimming up to the surface, but as the time for settlement draws near the behaviour alters. Changes in the internal chemistry of the body, we may suppose, direct its movements generally downwards, and certainly towards a solid object, whether rock, ship's hull, or floating plank. The larva dips to the solid surface and swims around and over it, touching down and rising repeatedly. What determines whether it should settle or no has not yet been elucidated. On the other hand, all observers are agreed that there is every appearance of searching one surface, in an apparently purposive manner, and, as likely as not, passing on and searching another and yet another before finally coming to rest. What is certain is that where spat has already settled more is likely to fall, and the assumption is that the spat already there exert a chemical attraction to those coming later. The same thing is suspected in larvae of other types of marine organism.

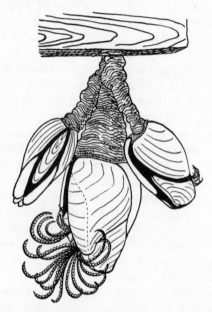

Stalked Ship- or Goose-barnacles on a floating timber.

So far, barnacles have been spoken of as if they were all alike, but there are two very distinct main types, the stalked Ship Barnacle, or Goose Barnacle, and the more common but less well-known Acorn Barnacle, which is not stalked, seen coating the rocks at low tide. In addition, there are several other forms that will merit at least passing attention.

In the Middle Ages, the geese that came mysteriously, as it seemed to the people then, out from the North, were believed to have developed from the stalked barnacles. The similarity between the rounded body and long neck of the goose and the rounded body and long stalk of the barnacle clearly influenced this belief, although there are many versions of how the one became transformed into the other. The Ship Barnacle is moored to its support by a long muscular stalk, and the body is enclosed in five plates, or shells. On one side of the body is a slit, through which can be protruded six pairs of curved legs, each leg consisting of two branches fringed with bristles. The Acorn Barnacle is constructed on a similar plan, except that there is no stalk and the shells form a turret seated directly on the rock surface, with a circular opening at the summit which can be closed by one pair of the shells. It sometimes happens that an Acorn Barnacle, usually so lifeless to all appearances, can be seen, just after the tide has ebbed, still protruding its legs. They come out with a grasping action, curling over and closing, like the action in clenching the fist, to be withdrawn and almost immediately protruded again in a rhythmic movement, as one might imagine the hand of the proverbial drowning man reaching out of the water to clutch the proverbial straw. After a while, the action ceases, the legs are completely withdrawn and the pair of shells at the summit close, sealing the barnacle within its fortress until the return of the tide. This action of the legs is the typical feeding movement, in which the bristled branches act as a self-closing sweep-net, capturing food and taking it in to the mouth.

It is traditional that one never should describe the feeding habits of a barnacle, without quoting the words (seemingly imperishable) of Thomas Henry Huxley, that the Barnacle is a "Crustacean fixed by its head and kicking the food into its mouth with its legs."

A quarter of a century or so after Vaughan Thompson's

exciting discovery about the true nature of the barnacle came the tremendous fillip to biological research from Darwin's enunciation of his Theory of Organic Evolution. For a half century or more, the search went on for facts to support—or, by a minority, to refute—the theory. In time the fact of Evolution became generally accepted, although the factors by which it is brought about are even now the subject for debate. It was natural that, among the

Acorn barnacles, with legs extended in feeding.

many types examined as evolutionary problems, barnacles should come under review. By what stages could an animal, rooted to the spot, and so like a mollusc in appearance, be derived from the same stock as the active and dissimilar crab, shrimp, and so forth? Was it possible to reconstruct its past history?

As always, evidence was sought from the fossil remains in the earliest rocks, and it is at this point that we can take up the story as given us in Withers' erudite monograph, completed in 1928. "Two main factors have militated against any great advance in our understanding of the fossil Cirripedia, and consequently in our ideas on the phylogeny of the group. One is the presence in the Paleozoic rocks of certain multi-valved fossils which have been regarded by many as primitive Cirripedes. The other, which is closely related to the first, is the occurrence in the Mesozoic rocks of numerous species of undoubted stalked Cirripedes considered to belong to the many-valved genus *Pollicipes*. Both factors, singly and together, have given rise to the prevailing belief that the ancestral Cirripede was a form with a large number of valves. This is the view expressed in the text-books." This is a sufficiently important statement to be quoted in full, together with Withers' later remarks, substantiated by subsequent workers in the same field, which can be stated briefly. The multi-valved fossils referred to, 200 million or more years old, probably represent an offshoot from the early stock from which starfishes and sea-urchins have sprung. The earliest undoubted fossil barnacle, and that was stalked, is a little over 170 million years old. Even during later geological periods, Cirripedes were still not numerous, so that as marine animals go, the barnacle arrived late in the evolutionary day. That is what Withers meant by the present day being the Age of Barnacles: it is that period in the history of their race when they have reached their greatest abundance in species and populations.

There must have been forerunners to the first known fossil barnacle, and it has been suggested that they may have had no hard parts capable of being fossilised, or that such hard parts as they had were so different in shape that they have not yet been recognised as the shells of barnacles. There is nothing remarkable in this last, for the museums contain many fossils the precise identity of which has not yet been established. At all events, there are no recognisable fossils to show the transition from the typical crustacean, as we know it, to the typical barnacle, and anything said about the ancestral forms of the present-day barnacle is no more than informed guesswork.

Some of the opinions are as follows. Annadale, the distinguished marine zoologist, writing in 1906, suggested that the ancestral barnacle was probably free-swimming—perhaps like the modern water-fleas or the cypris-stage in the present-day barnacles—but without the calcareous plates of its descendants. If so, then we should have expected some trace to have been found of the horny covering to the body. Withers, writing in 1915, said that: "We can as yet form only a vague idea of the ancestral Cirripede" but that there was no reason to assume that it was stalked—a sufficiently cautious pronouncement from an expert. Broch, a Danish zoologist, writing in 1922, is equally cautious and vague, while Ruedemann, the American, tried in 1924 to fix as the ancestors of our barnacles certain two-valved fossils in the Paleozoic rocks which almost certainly have no connexion with the barnacles. Another American, Van Name, in 1925, imagined the ancestral barnacle as a form very like the cypris-stage which lived buried in the mud, lying on its back, wafting water into its burrow with its legs, the water bringing oxygen and small particles of food. From such a form, in course of time, first by the development of protective calcareous plates, arose the beginnings of the bàrnacle as we know it now. Once it possessed this protective armour, its descendants would be capable of living in more exposed places and could in time, through random mutation acted upon by natural selection, acquire the necessary means for cementing the shell to the surface of a rock and all the other things needed to produce the modern barnacle.

It may seem an unnecessary digression to treat the evolution of the barnacle in such detail, and inappropriate to our theme since no barnacle has even achieved a life in fresh water, least of all an emergence on to dry land. But, as stated right at the beginning, my purpose here is not to prove a theory, but to state a theory and use the subsequent discussion as a means of expounding the biological principles which could support or refute it. For this, the barnacle story cannot be used to better purpose, for here we have an animal that has very truly "got the scientist guessing", and in some instances guessing rather wildly. It appears suddenly, using the word in the sense of geological time, in the form in which we know it to-day, looking outwardly like a totally different animal, the mollusc. Yet, if

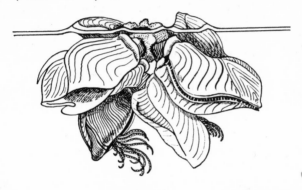

we are to attach any significance at all to the known details of its life-history, its ancestors must have sprung from the same stock as those of the totally different—so far as appearance goes—crabs, lobsters, shrimps and all the rest of the crustacea. It is a prime example upon which to test the validity of what I have called informed guessing.

The strongest arguments are found in the structure of the body of the barnacle, in those parts enclosed within the shells. The legs are comparable in design with those of other crustacea, especially those of sand-fleas and fresh-water shrimps. The nervous system is that of a crustacean. The method of feeding, also, is very like that of many other readily recognisable crustacea. There are, of course, other details, but these will be sufficient to show the type of evidence available. Finally, supporting evidence is seen in the fossils of the Acorn Barnacle-type. The first Acorn Barnacles appeared in the Upper Cretaceous, something like 100 million years ago, and the earliest of these leave little doubt that they were derived from stalked barnacles. Moreover, these early barnacles can be arranged in series showing the gradual loss of the stalk.

Over and above this more direct evidence, the scientist relies on what is called arguing by analogy. That is, he finds something similar to what he supposes to have taken place in one animal actually taking place in a related animal, and assumes that if this particular thing can happen to one organism it can happen to another. In other words, he puts his jigsaw together as far as he can despite the missing pieces, and completes the picture in his mind's eye, or with his imagination. It is the familiar method used by detectives in solving crime problems, which nobody thinks of questioning, except the counsel for the defence whose client is in desperate case.

Two analogous examples are given here, although others less spectacular could be adduced. The first is concerned with a relative of the sand-fleas, and the summary given here is from extensive observations made by Skogsberg and Vansell, two American zoologists, in 1928.

The sand-hoppers or sand-fleas, small and shrimp-like, live under the heaps of decaying seaweeds that accumulate along the drift-line. When we disturb these heaps they jump and hop in all directions in a manner that leaves little doubt of the derivation of their alternative name. They have come very near to abandoning a life in the sea for one ashore, except that they still need a moist situation and need the sea for breeding. Sand-fleas are represented by many species, and the order to which they belong, the Amphipoda, contains many more. Some of these live completely in the sea, many have found their way through the brackish waters of the estuaries into streams and lakes, where they are more familiar to us as freshwater shrimps. As a whole, therefore, the amphipods furnish us with an example of progression from the sea, on the one hand, up the beach, and, on the other hand, through the estuaries and into rivers, in both instances well on the way to becoming terrestrial. It is not with this aspect of them we are now concerned, but with the behaviour of a particular species studied on the Californian coasts.

This particular species has diverged from the main stream, so to speak, and has almost literally carved itself a special niche. Its mode of life is totally unlike that of a sand-flea or a freshwater shrimp, and yet it has accomplished this not by a change in structure but by a change in habits, by putting its limbs and other organs to a different use. Barely a quarter of an inch long, its body is compressed laterally, otherwise it has the general appearance along the back of the better-known wood-louse. That is, the body is armoured with a dozen transverse horny plates, joined and slightly overlapping. At the head end is a conspicuous but simple eye, in front of which are two pairs of antennae. These are followed, on the under-side and working backwards, by two pairs of jaws, two pairs of grasping legs, five pairs of walking legs, four pairs of swimming legs and finally a tail of sorts. So far, these same things could be said, more or less, of any of the Amphipods. The main difference between the one we are considering and the general run of its relatives is that it rarely uses the walking legs for walking, the swimming legs for swimming or the antennae for the purpose we usually associate with these organs. The antennae may sometimes be used as sensory-organs, or "feelers", but they also serve, and it may be their main function, for feeding. Added to all this, the animal spends its whole life on its back.

We could, with every justification, call this particular amphipod the sea-squirt flea, although I am not aware that it has been so-called until now. It lives on the body of a sea-squirt growing in sheltered parts of the rock-pools. Moreover, it is found on one kind of sea-squirt only, and usually then only if the squirt happens to be always submerged, or at least growing in moist cool crevices sheltered by overhanging seaweed. Even then, it is found only on those sea-squirts growing on rock surfaces most exposed to the wash of the tide. The "flea" is, therefore, fairly generalised in structure but highly specialised in habitat, and like the triangular wardrobe, occupying a highly specialised niche.

The female sea-squirt flea carries her eggs, and the young when they hatch, in a brood-pouch throughout the summer months. The 70 to 80 eggs hatch at different times, and the young ones are forced out of the pouch by the mother, using her grasping legs to squeeze the sides of the pouch. One investigator has described how they cling tenaciously to the maternal bristles and appear reluctant to leave their shelter. Eventually they depart, crawling on their backs, with the first four pairs of walking legs turned backwards to assist in locomotion, by pressing into the skin of the sea-squirt and pushing. Finding a suitable crevice in the sea-squirt skin, the young flea slides into it, the middle pair of walking legs remaining turned backwards (i.e. downwards) to hold on to the floor of the crevice. The other four pairs of walking legs grasp the edges of the crevice and pull them together, leaving only the antennae projecting, at the front end. This is, however, only a temporary move, one that ensures that all is set for the future.

Normally, the sea-squirt flea allows the lips of the crevice to part, exposing its lower surface, which is always uppermost, to the water. Then, beating gently with the swimming legs, it drives a current of water across its body, for breathing purposes. No doubt food, small particles of decaying matter as well as micro-organisms are brought in with the water and captured as food, but the main feeding is with the antennae. These are plentifully supplied with bristles, which become clogged with particles and micro-organisms. Then they are brought forward and cleaned by being passed through the jaws of the grasping legs, the food material being passed to the chewing jaws to masti-cate. It may sound far-fetched to have to speak of par-ticles and micro-organisms being masticated, but the young sea-squirt flea is only a hundredth of an inch long, and the jaws of even the fully-grown animal are no longer than this.

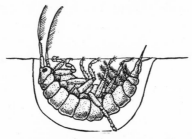

Sea-squirt flea in its home in the skin of a sea-squirt.

To increase in size, the young amphipod, like all the Crustacea, must moult its hard outer skin. So it grows in stages, by leaps and bounds, as it were, with long intervals between each leap—another cycle of activity, incident-ally. But it also means that the original crevice must be forsaken. Then the growing animal wanders to another part of the sea-squirt. Having selected a spot—and it does not take just the first place it comes to—it stretches its walking legs out to either side, lying on its back of course, and takes hold of the sea-squirt's skin with the minute pincer-like hooks at the ends of the walking legs. Then it begins slowly to pull. The tough skin as slowly yields. Gradually the animal sinks into the skin until finally it is so deep down that the edges of the cavity so formed can be pulled over it, the whole operation taking several hours.

Earlier on, the word selection has been used, implying that this animal with its limited nervous equipment is capable of exercising a choice. That is how it appears to an observer, and it seems inescapable that, in spite of its low position in the animal scale, an amphipod does exercise a choice. For example, it was found that if persuaded from its burrow and put into an aquarium on another kind of sea-squirt, or on a sponge, or some other soft-bodied marine animal, it makes no attempt to settle down. On the contrary, it crawls around, laboriously and restlessly, trying first this and then that, until it finally succumbs, apparently from exhaustion.

It seems reasonable enough to assume that should a subsequent mutation result in a sea-squirt flea having limy salts in its outer skin—in other words, the beginnings of shells covering the body—the way would be open to the evolution of an animal of the barnacle type from an otherwise typical crustacean. This may even be the explanation of the absence of ancestral barnacles from the fossil record. If the sea-squirt flea were extinct instead of living to-day, all we should find of it would be the remains of an apparently typical amphipod. The soft body of the sea-squirt itself would be unlikely to form a recognisable fossil, and we should not have the slightest clue as to the peculiar way of life of the amphipod.

This chosen example also has another significance. The question is often posed whether change of habit precedes change of form in evolution, or vice-versa. Probably the truth is that sometimes the one and sometimes the other comes first. The behaviour of the sea-squirt flea suggests that, at least sometimes, the change in behaviour may come first.

CHAPTER ELEVEN

PSYCHOLOGY OF THE PINHEAD LARVA

IF we say that a barnacle larva exercises a choice, it must be on the assumption that the larva is not merely the plaything of external physical forces, but that it does, in fact, contribute something from within itself to its own destiny. The word "choice" may have been used loosely in such a connotation, for want of a better word, or to describe some manifestation of behaviour that has not yet been fully analysed. Even so, the fact that more than one scientist, observing the activities of marine larvae has been driven to use the word, suggests that what they have seen looks uncommonly like the familiar attribute of human behaviour. By the unwritten rules of their profession, scientists should speculate, but they should also take the first opportunity to test their speculations. This has been done for the larvae of a marine worm which is even lower in the scale than a barnacle. It has also been done for the larvae of oysters and others. It is convenient, however, to take this particular worm because of the masterly work and summing up given us by Dr Douglas Wilson, in the *Annales de l'Institut scientifiques* for 1952.

Ophelia bicornis—a delightful name—is found in a few bays and estuaries along the Atlantic coast of France and northern Spain, and, so far, in one place only in the British Isles, the estuary of the River Exe, in Devon. It lives in isolated communities in clean loose sand churned by violent tidal currents. At one time, it would have been assumed that the larvae of an animal with such a restricted habitat settled indiscriminately on the sea-bottom at the end of a definite span of larval life, and that only those that happened by chance to find the right place survived. It is now known that they not only search for the correct habitat but are able to delay metamorphosis until this has been found. These properties must obviously form part of that natural selection we have been examining. In other words, they contribute to the evolutionary process, and their study is therefore an integral part of our discussion. What is more, the investigations carried out by Wilson, and others, come very near to research into psychology at its lowest levels, a kind of micro-psychology, in fact. It is of interest, therefore, not only to see the results they obtained, but also how they set about studying the psychology of a simple organism the size of a pin's head, and at a stage in its life history when internal organs, and least of all a central nervous system, have hardly had time to develop.

To understand fully the line of the enquiry, it is necessary to recall certain elementary principles. A number of unicellular organisms are known to migrate towards the light. If contained within a small trough of water in the dark their wanderings are erratic. If, however, a beam of light is allowed to fall on one end of the trough, they will migrate towards it. The organisms are said to be positively phototactic. There are others, on the other hand, which habitually migrate away from the light and are said to be negatively phototactic. In addition to phototaxis, there are other forms of automatic response, or taxes, such as the moving towards or away from a chemical substance (chemotaxis), moving into or away from a warm patch (thermotaxis), and so on. The situation can be approximately compared with the remote control of a pilotless plane, with an inner mechanism responding to an external stimulus. In the case of the living organism we are as yet unable to say what the internal mechanism is but we can observe and test the effect of the stimulus.

Wilson set out to determine whether it was the result of

a number of such taxes which brought the *Ophelia* larvae finally to settle. First of all, he found that the worms were particularly abundant in the Bullhill Bank, where they numbered 200 to the square metre. In the sand of the Salthouse Lake, however, a short distance away, they occurred sparsely in a few places and moderately abundantly in one narrow sand ridge. In the area of the Polesands, where they were formerly in the greatest abundance, they are now found in a limited area only. The Bullhill Bank sand is coarser than that of the Salthouse Lake, and

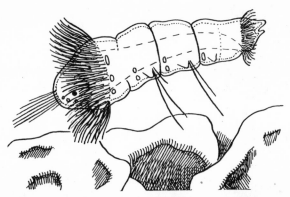

Larva of *Ophelia* searching sand-grains for a resting place.

cleaner, with less silt. On the other hand, it seems that the sand in the areas on the French coast is finer than that at Bullhill Bank.

Larvae were kept under laboratory conditions and samples of the Bullhill and the Salthouse sands were made available to them. They were seen to test and enter the layers of sand and to settle only on those most suitable for adult life. They chose the Bullhill sands most easily even when the Salthouse sands had been washed clean of their silt. If the Salthouse sand were both washed and re-graded until it was indistinguishable to the human eye from the

Bullhill sand, they still settled hardly at all in it. This suggested that it was not necessarily the shape or size of the grains that influenced their choice, so steps were taken to test whether there might be some chemical property that decided them. A sample of sand was boiled, to sterilise it. The larvae were poisoned by it. Sand washed with ether, alcohol or acetone or cold dilute acids still proved unacceptable. On the other hand, samples of this same Salthouse sand, unacceptable in its virgin state could be made acceptable to them if heated to redness, and especially if afterwards treated with hot acids and alkalis, and more particularly if treated with finely divided activated charcoal.

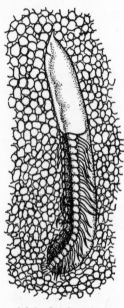

Adult *Ophelia* lying on sand.

Attention was then paid to the Bullhill sand, which is naturally acceptable to the larvae. They settled on it even more readily after it had been heated to redness, and even more still if treated with activated charcoal. On the other hand, if heated in distilled water for two to three hours it was less acceptable to them, although soaking in fresh water at room temperature for a long period made no difference to their settling on it.

These results, although interesting, were not very illuminating, so a different method of approach was tried. Bullhill sand was soaked in sea-water for several weeks. By this means it was hoped to take into solution any chemical property the sand might contain. The water was then filtered off, but on its own, and without the sand, the larvae could not be induced to settle. Another experiment was tried with a container of sea-water, having a layer of Bull-hill sand at the bottom, so arranged that the larvae were under natural conditions, except that they were prevented from making contact with the sand-grains. They still failed to settle. This suggested that the determining factor in their settlement was not a chemical in the sand itself.

Although microscopic examination of the Bullhill and Salthouse sands revealed no distinction between them, if a sample of the first were washed and then dried and dropped on to the water from a height of 1 cm. it sank, while the Salthouse sand dropped in the same way floated. The floatability of a sand can be decreased by heating to redness, and by treatment with hot acids and alkalis and with activated charcoal. It can be altered by exposure to weather, and it will increase and decrease from time to time by other natural means. It can be increased by repeated wetting and drying and by friction against silk or copper gauze, producing static electric charges on the grains in dry air, or by altering the molecular surface of the grains. These and many other physical and chemical factors were considered and tested.

Perhaps the one solid thing to emerge concerned the size of the sand-grains. A larva settling undergoes meta-morphosis before it can start growing into the adult worm. Before metamorphosis can take place, the larva must enter the sand. If the grains are too small, the spaces be-tween them will not permit this. If the grains are too large, the spaces between them are liable to become choked with fine grains. So after weighing everything up, Wilson could say no more than that the larvae "favour very clean sands which are mainly free from some repel-lent factor of unknown nature. The sands are fairly coarse and loose. Rounded grains are probably more favourable than sharply angular ones. The optimum grain size seems to lie between about 0.20 mm. and 0.45 mm. in diameter but considerable latitude is allowable". In any case, the larvae appeared to react adversely to factors present in the sand that would be unsuitable to their adult life. It may even be that the circumstances to which they react favourably are produced by adults already living in the sand. It could be one of several other things, or a combination of many of the factors tested, or all of them, together with others hitherto unsuspected. Wilson may have been unsuccessful in pressing his investigations to a final conclusion, but he has given us a useful illustration of an animal's reaction to its environment, in the vital early stages of its career, of a blind foresight in which the future needs of the adult must be met before the larva will settle, and of the delicate balance upon which the survival of the more selective or specialised species depends. In fact, his researches give so much food for thought that it is difficult to know which point to take first.

The thought uppermost in my mind while reading the final pages of his report was that the combination of factors which ensure the survival of the individual, and, when taken on a large scale, the survival of the species, can be compared with the lock of a safe. A burglar opening a safe has to find out the combination of numbers. He must get these exactly right before the door will swing open. If we are to believe the crime stories of fiction, he must fiddle with the lock, trying one number after another, but it is only when he has them all lined up that the restraining tongue of the lock moves in the right direction, and this only when the last one clicks into place. In other words, the settlement of the larva takes place only when the correct combination of physical and chemical factors are present to make the organism's internal mechanism work in a certain direction.

Conversely, the same comparison can be made for the work of the investigator himself, that it is only when he has unravelled all the factors and clicked the last one into place that he sees the solution to his problem.

Keeping the lock simile in mind, it is more easy to see the significance of the gene-mutation. If so many factors must be satisfied to ensure the survival of the individual, any single change, even a very small one, in the organisation of its body can exert tremendous influence for good or ill. As a rule, any change is more likely to be a disadvantage and lead to the non-survival of the individual, and through the individuals to the extinction of the race or species. This is what is meant when we say that the great majority of mutations are lethal. On the other hand, it also means that any mutation which is not so disastrous can lead to a complete change either in the structure of a part of the body, or a group of parts, or in the behaviour and the habitat of the organism. It can have the same critical and far-reaching effect as the withdrawal of the tongue of a lock leading to the opening of a safe.

Another of the many thoughts stimulated by this piece of research, and by others along the same lines, is that, given time, it is theoretically possible to explain the behaviour of all organisms satisfactorily in terms of the ultimate physical and chemical components. It is possible, taking these one at a time in their simplest expressions, to describe each one precisely and in suitably accurate terminology. It is, however, the synthesis of these separate reactions that is difficult to describe adequately without using expressions usually applied to the more conscious behaviour of human beings. It then becomes a moot point how far we are justified in describing as a "choice" the sum total of external stimuli calling forth an innate behaviour pattern. Certainly in the larva of a marine worm, if choice it be, it is of a simpler order than we customarily associate with comparable actions in ourselves. Equally it is debatable whether, if we could analyse sufficiently minutely our own behaviour, we should not find our own choices dependent upon similar, but more complex, sets of reactions. Perhaps further aspects of the behaviour of the *Ophelia* larva will shed light on this.

Apparently *Ophelia* spawns on a rising tide, which makes me think of the fragmentation of the purse-sponge and the difficulty I had in catching it in the act. There is an obvious advantage in this, that the larvae will not be carried by currents out to sea, but are more likely to be able to settle in the normal habitat. The first action of the larvae is to swim towards the surface, showing themselves to be positively phototactic. After swimming in the surface waters for a period, they swim down to the bottom and explore it. In doing so, they show themselves to be negatively phototactic. They push their way into the interstices of the sand and, if the soil is suitable, lay hold of the sand-grains so firmly that it is difficult to dislodge them. If, for reasons that it has not been possible to ascertain, the soil is unsuitable, they release their hold and swim up once more to the surface. In this return to the surface they are presumably once more positively phototactic. After swimming around for another space of time, they make their way once more to the bottom to explore another site. Again if unsuited they will return to the surface. Apparently they are able to postpone metamorphosis for days or even weeks in this search for a suitable site.

This same story can be told of the larvae of other marine organisms with more or less variations to it, and it raises several very perplexing problems. First of all there is this repeated change from the quality of being positively phototactic to that of being negatively phototactic. We are accustomed to thinking of these properties as fixed and characteristic of a particular organism, or of a particular stage in the life of that organism. We are, moreover, aware that the transition from the one to the other can result from some physiological change in an organism. Or, at least, we can suspect that it is so. For example, when in summer the young queen ants swarm for their nuptial flight, they fly up into the air after having previously spent their time exclusively underground. After mating, when presumably a physiological change has taken place, they return to earth and make their utmost endeavour to shed their wings and burrow down into the earth once more. Before the flight, they were negatively phototactic and positively geotactic, and these things make them stay underground. At the ascent for the nuptial flight, under the influence, it is believed, of meteorological conditions, they have become positively phototactic and negatively geotactic. This makes them fly up. After mating, presumably as the result this time of an internal change resulting from mating, they have once more reverted to being negatively phototactic and positively geotactic. So they come to earth again and burrow into it. This is an explanation we can accept, albeit with some caution, merely because it is feasible to believe in an environmental change or an internal change being responsible for the variations in the taxes. In other words, the explanation is plausible, and possibly feasible. It is difficult, on the other hand, to see any reason why there should be this comparable change in the nature of the *Ophelia* larva merely because it was unsuited in its search for a place in which to metamorphose.

The next difficult point to understand is why, when the larva remains unsuited in its search for a site, the metamorphosis should be delayed, often for a long period beyond the normal span of its larval life. It is next to impossible to suggest a reason for it, especially when we remember that in other instances it has been found not only that the larval period is thus delayed, but that in the end some larvae at least will metamorphose at the surface of the water, where all the normal stimuli are lacking for such a procedure. It is as though there is a drive to metamorphose, that normally this drive reaches fruition under the stimulus of the appropriate complex of external conditions, but that ultimately it must be fulfilled even in the absence of those conditions.

The settlement of larvae seems, in the abstract, a simple enough affair, but in addition to the hazards just discussed there are others. In looking into the question of the non-settlement of the larvae, Wilson found that the period of postponement varied from one brood to another, that it depended on hereditary factors as well as conditions of the environment. He has reason to suppose that it was influenced by temperature; by the conditions of the water, by the degree of ripeness of the eggs and the sperms at the time of fertilisation, and by the health of the larvae. All these, he believed, influenced the length of the larval life as well as the larval reactions towards the sites they were exploring.

Although it was not possible to determine completely the conditions required for a normal settlement and metamorphosis, it was possible to establish with a fair degree of confidence certain of these factors. First, that the larva prefers a soil of rounded sand-grains, although grains of other shapes did not necessarily inhibit settlement. Secondly, that the sand must be a certain degree of cleanliness and yet the grains must bear sufficient of the minute organic growths that would serve the adult for food. Thirdly, there was no obvious chemical attraction, in which case the presence of the necessary food-materials on the grains must be detected by touch. Fourthly, the larvae were not influenced, as happens in many other species, such as Acorn Barnacles, by larvae already settled. Fifthly, they would not settle where certain other organisms were already in occupation. The presence of lugworms in the sand, for example, was a deterrent to settlement.

This does not mean that none of the larvae ever make mistakes and settle where the soil is unsuitable. It is conceivable that they do, and suffer the consequences. It is not the mistakes that call for comment but "the proved ability of the larvae to recognise with such complete certainty their own sand when they first make contact with it." And we may sum up, again in Wilson's words: "The larvae, when settling, react not to one factor only, but to a pattern of factors, in which cleanliness, or the presence or absence of some repellent factor, often associated with sands inhabited by a normal sand fauna, is of special significance. ... This ability, inborn and inherited, is a fundamental characteristic of the species and we are as yet only beginning to comprehend how the recognition is made".

It is easy enough to say that evolution is the result of random mutation acted upon by natural selection. It is possible to give the more elementary and somewhat gross examples of what is meant by natural selection. Usually these take the form of instances in which a predator weeds out the species on which it preys. If the investigations on *Ophelia* show us nothing else, they expose the almost limitless number of factors and combinations of factors comprising that natural selection. This taken in conjunction with the equally limitless opportunities for gene-mutation, together with the variable use made of the inherited characters and potentialities, make it possible for almost anything to happen.

CHAPTER TWELVE

SPONGE-CRAB SHOWS ITS PACES

WHEN on holiday in Cornwall, in the days before I had begun even to pretend I was a marine zoologist, I walked out at low tide on a narrow reef of rocks, perhaps a quarter of a mile long. I had been searching the rocks, somewhat idly while walking, and having arrived at the seaward end of the rocks it suddenly occurred to me that I had not seen a single crab. This, of course, was absurd. On my way back I searched more carefully, but without turning over any stones or seaweeds. Crabs were everywhere. Small, medium, large; red, green, variegated, on seaweed, wedged under stones; they were everywhere. Camouflage is a master art of these decapod crustaceans.

But then we have the anomaly, that in spite of their ability to hide, in spite also of their heavy armour and the somewhat fearsome claws, crabs seem to be preyed upon by a far greater ring of enemies than any other marine animal. Fish eat them. Conger, wrasse, flounder swallow them whole or seize them in the mouth and bang them on the rocks to crack their armour. Octopus find them easy prey. Birds eat them: gulls, eider duck, waders. Rats invade the shore, sometimes by day, but more especially by night, at low tide. They may take carrion, or even other shore-living animals, but certainly they take crabs, and one wonders how they contrive to break through the defence of the brandished gaping claws. I have often wondered, too, how the eider, which lives so much on crabs, diving to the bottom for them, manage to seize them without injury to themselves. There is even one record of pigs having invaded the shore to root for crabs.

No doubt each predator has its particular trick for coping with the stout pair of nippers, and in this connexion, an observation by M. R. Raut, in the *Journal of the Bombay Natural History Society* for 1943 is worth quoting in full: "We were watching a flock of whimbrel (Elephanta Island, Bombay Harbour, 10 January 1943) on a mangrove-bordered mud-shore, swarming with fiddler-crabs (*Gelasimus* sp.) of all sizes. The bird caught the crab by its 'fiddle', lifted it up into the air and then sharply jerked its head. The fiddle broke off and the whimbrel methodically dropped the fiddle, picked up the owner and swallowed him. The place was littered with inedible claws. The size and shape of the whimbrel's beak also appeared to help it extract the crabs from their holes. The ease with which the crustacean discards its claws and limbs is often quoted as an adaptive device to help it to escape. In this case the crab is hoisted on its own petard!"

It would be interesting, if one had the time, to compile a complete list of the enemies of crabs. It would be long and varied. Certainly in addition to gulls and eider, terns, razorbills, auks, guillemots and cormorants take them fairly readily in their diet, and possibly other birds do; and there are probably more that take them occasionally. Seals also include them in the daily catch, and there is, of course, the crab-eater seal of the Antarctic.

One of the more noticeable features of the shore at low-tide is the number of dead crabs lying on the beach or between the rocks. There are, of course, the remains of the gull's meal, but these have a characteristic pattern. In the middle is the upturned shell picked fairly clean, with the legs and claws lying around where they have been pulled off and dropped. And usually a gull's feather or two and droppings to leave the identity of the predator in no doubt. Over and above these are the smashed carcases, washed limp and unresisting by every wavelet, or lying sprawled, high and dry. Sometimes they are few in number, sometimes the shore is fairly littered with them, and they have the appearance of death due to having been smashed, dashed on the rocks, perhaps, or stove in by pebbles churned by the waves. They could, of course, be crabs that have died of a disease, showing a post-mortem battering.

In addition there is cannibalism, which appears to reach a relatively high percentage. It is not merely the devouring of dead individuals, or the killing of sickly members, which is by no means unknown in many other animal species. Unless appearances are deceptive, the larger crabs do, in fact, prey on the smaller, chasing and killing them. This is the comment usually made, at all events, but it is very rare to find someone who has actually seen the killing take place, and it may be just another myth. On the other hand, crabs do seem afflicted with a propensity for being unable to keep their fingers off anything lying about. A good illustration of this is seen in the story of the disappearing spat. Oyster spat laid down in rows in an experimental tank, for studying the growth rate of the oyster, were found destroyed—they had not disappeared so much as been extinguished. Then someone noticed that, unknown to those in charge of the experiment, a small crab had been introduced into the aquarium. It was seen to walk along a row of spat and crush each one in turn with its claws—a trick reminiscent of the treatment of crocuses by sparrows, or of any article of value left within reach of a child or a puppy. Whether it is indicative of an advanced mental development, budding curiosity or mere destructiveness is a question Science has not yet settled.

We may excuse the child on the grounds that it is learning to use its fingers, or the puppy that it must exercise its growing teeth, but the crab, like the sparrow, seems to have an innate tendency towards destructiveness. On the rare occasions off the English coast, when a calm sea with crystal clear water flows back over a sandy beach with scattered seaweed-covered rocks, an observer may watch over the side of a dinghy the crabs swarming. Their numbers are often quite surprising, having been hidden in the rocks during the ebb-tide. Using the sandy bottom as an arena, they run rapidly this way and that, forever brandishing their claws at every fellow they meet. They give a firm appearance of being always ready to destroy and of being always on the defensive. There seems here a close parallel with the destructiveness of the human child that has been ill-treated. The subject is one worthy of further study. The suggestion has already been put forward, quite seriously, and probably with truth, that carrion crows attack the nests of game-birds if their nests are shot through. Perhaps the fox, whose natural prey is rats and rabbits, raids the fowl's roost as a result of persecution. The list could be extended. It has been found, also, in a careful series of observations, that some rats are habitually bullied by their fellows, and that their behaviour, as a consequence, departs radically from that normal for the species.

These items are not, as might appear, raised in a frivolous vein, for the point I am trying to make is that the simple formula used to explain organic evolution—random variation acted upon by natural selection—is inadequate, unless our definition of natural selection is broadened beyond what it is usually taken to mean. And, as a rule, too little account is taken, in my opinion, of psychological factors, especially in the lower animals.

It could be that in making these remarks the case for natural selection is not being fairly presented, that it could, and is, used to include psychological factors. In that event, my comment would still be that too little is made of them in regard to the lower animals. Certainly the more stereotyped view is that expressed in that somewhat outworn phrase, the struggle for existence. So far as crabs are concerned, even in this field the issue is somewhat contradictory, largely perhaps because we do not yet possess as full a knowledge of all the facts as we should like. Thus, in crabs, as in all animals, the weeding-out of individuals by predators or other natural forces, should be one of the principal items in natural selection. Here is what we find in two species of crabs. In the common shore crab, each mature female lays something under 200,000 eggs in a season. The female of the edible crabs lays up to 3,000,000 in one season. In both, we may presume, the populations will remain static, on the average, over a period of years. In that case, the absolute mortality for the shore crab is one-fifteenth of that of the edible crab. The former lives largely between tide-marks, where the physical conditions are more severe and where, as we have seen, it is beset by enemies from sea, air and land. The edible crab is larger, more heavily armoured and armed, and does not have to defend itself against attacks on three fronts, nor does it suffer, one would suppose, from such severe physical conditions, since it lives mainly in the offshore waters. The fact that man preys on it merely results in local depletions in its populations.

Arguing from first principles, the production of three million as against two hundred thousand eggs give fifteen times the opportunity for the emergence of random variations in the offspring. Under natural selection, therefore, the edible crab should be more highly evolved than the shore crab. On the other hand, the shore-crab is subject to a greater pressure from natural selection by the physical conditions of the inter-tidal zone.

Admittedly, what follows is highly speculative because a full and close analysis of the behaviour of the shore-crab has not been made, and even less is known about that of the edible crab. It is possible, arguing from what is known of both species and, by analogy with what has been gathered from one other species in particular, to put forward a hypothesis, which is plausible and possibly feasible. It will be seen, from evidence to be brought forward later, that it is possible for the edible crab to endure conditions between tide-marks. It is, also, quite a common thing to find young edible crabs in the littoral at low-tide. The physical conditions are not, therefore, an absolute barrier to the edible crab taking up permanent residence in the littoral. My suggestion is that the shore-crab has been able to do so because of a two-fold advantage: its natural camouflage and its natural adaptability, both of which, in their different ways, are factors affecting the further evolution of a species. The shore-crab, moreover, shows a progressive tendency, progressive, that is, in our sense of tending away from a marine to a terrestrial life, and is, in fact, showing signs of following the route which the ancestors of the more successful terrestrial groups probably followed. Shore-crabs will move up rivers, into water that can only be mildy brackish. They can be seen in the most surprising places in muddy creeks, often well away from the shore line.

This chapter started with the assertion that crabs are masters of the art of concealment. This may be of several kinds, according to the species. First, in shore living or sublittoral species, the colour tends to harmonise with the surroundings, except in such as the fiddler crabs, where the male is apt to be brilliantly, even startlingly coloured, the female being sombrely coloured, in the manner more familiar to us in birds. The fiddlers live, however, in burrows in the sand, which is another way of effacing a prominent body. Secondly, there is concealment by the shape of the carapace, as the hard shell of the body is called. An example from our own coasts is the circular crab, which, when legs and claws are drawn in, presents a fair representation of a smooth, whitish, rounded pebble. In most crabs, the edge of the carapace is saw-edged or toothed, serving to break up the hard outline. But the most remarkable camouflage is seen in crabs living on coral beaches, which are so shaped and coloured as to be practically indistinguishable from the fragments of coral-rock. Thirdly, there is concealment by burrowing, either a burrow forming a more or less permanent residence, as in the fiddler crabs of the tropics, already mentioned, or in a temporary burrow, as in our masked crab which sinks into the sand but moves its ground as occasion demands. There is also the more temporary sinking into the sand for refuge, as with the shore crab. Finally, there are those species which decorate the back with seaweeds, sea-squirts, sponges and the like. These include the spider

Circular crabs showing a resemblance to pebbles.

crab and the sponge crab, both of which are deserving of closer attention later.

Animals endowed with protective colouring or shape, or both, may make use of these in two ways, static or dynamic. In all, the protective values are effective only when at rest: anything moving immediately catches the eye. The distinction between the static and the dynamic use can be best illustrated by more familiar examples than those found in the sea. In the static class of use are included such things as the mottled plumage of the young plover which "freezes" at first alarm and stays quite still, the plumage harmonising in a general sense with the sand. A dynamic use is found in the moths in which the pattern of the wings resembles that of bark, but who orientate themselves on coming to rest so that there is the maximum continuity between the lines on the bark and those on the insect's wings. This is seen more positively when the moth settles on weathered timber, against which it would be comparatively obvious but for this orientation. In the young plover, the use made of the colour is due to an inborn nervous reflex having no relation to the background. The young bird would do exactly the same if it were standing on a black or a white background which threw its form and colours into bold relief. In the moth, the seemingly purposive or even intelligent action is automatic, but directed through the eye, as in the colour-change of a chameleon, or a plaice, which more slowly changes colour to suit its background.

It is doubtful if an animal's protective colouring is ever used intelligently, that is, with an awareness of the advantages to be gained, although some instances look extraordinarily like it. I once made close observation of a half-grown dabchick. When first I came across it, swimming in a shallow, narrow stream, it fled swimming. Always when approached it would do the same, to come to rest in front of a gnarled and rotten stump, against which, in one position, it was practically invisible even at three yards' distance. I watched it once, face to face, at six feet range, from the other bank of the stream. For half an hour it was motionless, and would have stayed so longer had I not become cramped and moved suddenly. This looked very like an awareness, on the part of the bird, that only in that one place, and in the one position, it was perfectly camouflaged.

Some crabs behave very like the dabchick, giving an appearance of purposive or quasi-intelligent behaviour. Romanes, over half-a-century ago, found that crabs had tolerably high learning abilities. Proffering a crab food, he would tap its claw sharply when it made to take it. After seven repetitions of this mild punishment, a crab would learn not to put its claw out to proffered food. Similar experiments, with similar results, have been made more recently on octopus by J. Z. Young. Conscious behaviour lies in inhibiting a natural instinct. Human beings have the ability to exercise conscious control (i.e. inhibit) after a minimum of trial and error. They can also anticipate adverse consequences of an action and inhibit, by a process we call reasoning, without the necessary trial by experience. But we do not always do so. In one particular, at least, then, the nervous ganglia, which do duty in a crab for what in ourselves we call a brain, work along the same lines but not with the same promptitude or with the same efficiency. To be conscious that in a given position, wearing particular colours, one is inconspicuous, demands a degree of conceptual thought of which we can be fairly sure a crab is not capable.

At the same time, our understanding of the nervous system and brain, whether of ourselves or of animals, is still somewhat inadequate, and from that limited amount we can appreciate that there is often a thin line dividing the more elaborated instinctive actions and the rudiments of an intelligence. If, as I have tried to show, there is so strong a relationship between all living things, then any human characteristic must have its beginnings lower in the scale. Intelligence must therefore begin at some low point in the animal scale, in a barely recognisable form. For that reason, zoologists prefer to speak of it as a plastic behaviour, though how this differs from a rudimentary intelligence nobody is at all sure.

There is one form of camouflage in crabs which seems to come very near being used with a dawning intelligence. For it, we must go to the spider crab which bears on its carapace a number of minute hooks. The young spider crab, without previous learning, nips off pieces of seaweed, sea-squirt and sponges and hooks them on to its back. So it is rendered invisible against its background. This much, we may be sure, is instinctive. Now take the crab and put it on a bed of, say, green seaweeds and it will strip off the pieces of brown seaweed, replacing them with fragments that will harmonise with its background. Or, again, if we take a spider crab so decorated and place it on a sandy background, it will, as soon as released, literally rush over to a growth where it is likely to be invisible, and settle down. No doubt such things are due to automatic responses to stimuli received through the eye, but they look very like something more—a choice coupled with an awareness of danger. It is a matter upon which a dogmatic opinion is impossible, even as it is so very much a matter of doubt how much of human choice is an automatic response to stimuli received through the eye.

The speed of the spider crab's reaction to an unsuitable background was brought home to me vividly some years ago, when I was photographing. Having taken a picture of a spider crab on its natural background, I wanted one of the beast on a contrasting background. In the end, it was necessary to hold it by pressing one finger on its carapace and work the shutter as I withdrew my finger. The resulting picture shows the ripples. Indeed, photographing marine animals under water gives a very different idea of the speeds they use from that we normally have by watching them when the tide has gone out. A starfish, really on the move, is by no means the sluggish animal we are apt to imagine it.

In the earlier part of this chapter I have deliberately invited comparison of the actions of crabs with those of higher animals, even with those of humans. This may have appeared unduly extravagant since their nervous system is of a simple type, and a brain, as we understand it in the vertebrates, does not exist. The nervous system is closely similar to that of insects. There is the usual ventral nerve cord, with a series of ganglia, with nerves running from each to supply the internal organs and the limbs. The ventral nerve cord ends in front in a pair of ganglia, connected by a pair of nerves passing round the oesophagus to link with another pair of ganglia, supplying nerves chiefly to the sense-organs. A ganglion is merely a knot of nerve-cells, whereas a brain is a bigger knot, or better still a group of knots. But although a brain is so much more complicated, it works, so far as we can tell on the same lines as a ganglion, but can do more work, and more efficient work. In volume, but not in specialisation of the tissues, the cerebral ganglia of a large crab are comparable with the brain of a mouse. The nervous system of a crab, as I have said, is comparable with that of an insect, and it is chiefly through the study of insects that we have been compelled to adopt the phrase "plastic behaviour" because it comes so near to appearing to be intelligent behaviour. If, according to my postulate, the thing we call intelligence in human beings must have started lower in the scale of animal life, as everything else about us has done, then I am prepared to believe that its beginning can be seen in the Crustacea, at least. To elaborate this viewpoint, we cannot do better than study some experiments carried out by Dembowska, in 1926, on the sponge crab.

The sponge crab (*Dromia*) habitually carries on its back a sponge, held in position by the last two pairs of walking legs, which are specially modified for that purpose. The sponge fits the carapace exactly, like a cap on the human head. It is concave and smooth on the lower side, where it rests on the carapace, and, to the early zoologists, it constituted a puzzle. Renier, in the middle of last century, assumed that the sponge larva must have settled on the crab's back, and, as it developed, had overgrown the carapace. Vosmaer, the Dutch zoologist, later in the century, influenced by the smooth under-surface, thought the crab must have taken a sponge that was growing on a bi-valve shell, to use for this purpose. In fact, it is the result of a neat piece of cutting and fitting, and *Dromia* will, in default of a sponge, use sea-squirts, seaweeds, rags, paper or anything that can be cut, fitted or moulded to its purpose.

Dembowska was more interested in how the crab accomplished this, and what it would do if deprived of its covering. Specimens of *Dromia* were kept under observation in sea-water aquaria, and to reduce the behaviour of the crabs to simple and understandable proportions, sheets of paper were supplied them, after their sponge caps had been removed. The method used was to tear, with the claws, a piece of paper that exactly fitted the carapace. The noteworthy feature was that there was great individual variation in the way this was done. One crab might lie on its back on top of the paper to tear it; another would hold it up. Or one would start at a corner of the paper, another would start at the side, and another would start in the middle. Some would tear the paper in a clockwise direction, others would achieve the same end in an anti-clockwise direction. Usually the same individual would use the same method, every time, but this was not invariable. It sometimes happened that a crab would put the whole of the paper over its back, in such a position that the forward edge of it lay just behind its eyes, and then tear it, suggesting that sight was not necessary to a successful conclusion of the operation. Or it would only partially complete the operation and walk away with a circle of paper covering its back and the rest of the sheet trailing behind. In such a case, it would later sever the unwanted piece. Some crabs turned the paper as they tore it, others kept the paper stationary and themselves revolved to complete the tearing. It was also noticed that if the paper did not fit well after cutting, or did not set well on the back, the crab would press or smooth it down with its claws to mould it to the correct shape.

When a large stone, bearing a sponge, was put into an aquarium alongside a crab deprived of its covering, it would cut a furrow in the sponge of such dimensions that when the piece within the furrow was lifted off it exactly fitted its back. If the stone bore several sponges, the crab would take the one most readily suited to its needs for size and shape. And in all cases, the trimming of a sponge to fit showed the same variation of treatment as was given to the paper. On the other hand, occasionally a crab would go seriously wrong and cut so small a sponge that it would cover no more than the lower part of its back.

Doubtless all this can be explained in terms of an inherent behaviour pattern comparable to the rhythmic movements of the plumose sea-anemone and the activity cycles of the lugworm. In them there were individual variations, but the individual variations in the crab cutting a sponge, or paper, were very much wider, showing a greater plasticity in behaviour so that it had almost the appearance of an intelligence.

If the choice and cutting of the covering for its back was the manifestation of an innate behaviour, how are we to translate the further results of Dembowska's experiments? For example, if the sponge were removed from the back of a crab, one of four ways would be used to replace it. One crab would grasp the sponge on both sides with its claws, fall on to its back, pulling the sponge up as it fell. Then, it would support it with its legs, with the concavity downmost until the flattened, leading edge, which exactly fits the crab's head, pointed towards its tail. Holding it in its position, it would then slowly turn until, standing on its head and gripping the sponge in the appropriate place with the fourth and fifth legs, let it slip exactly into place. The second method employed was to walk backwards to the sponge, grip it with the fourth and fifth legs and fling it exactly on to the back.

Another method was to walk head foremost to the

Sponge crab defeats all attempts to deprive it of its cloak.

sponge, continue walking over it until the hind edge of the abdomen was touching the near edge of the sponge, grasp it with the fourth and fifth legs, and again in one movement, fling it into place. The fourth method, much the least clever, was simply to turn on its back, so as to lie in the cavity of the sponge, then turn it this way and that until, by sheer trial and error, it was in the right position for carrying.

The next test was to remove the sponge and place it on the floor of the aquarium with its concavity downwards. One of three methods would be used to deal with this. The crab might merely creep under the sponge, grasp it with the carrying legs and in one movement restore it to its former place on the back. The less brilliant crab would turn the sponge over so that its concave side was uppermost, then use one of the four methods already detailed for this position. The third method was to grasp the sponge with the claws, after which the crab would fall on to its back and fit the sponge in place using the first of the methods described for dealing with it when laid down with its concave side uppermost.

If the sponge was placed with the concave side uppermost and filled with stones, one crab would tip the sponge up to empty it of stones, after having walked round it for a while as if non-plussed. Or it might push the stones out one by one. It was noticed that when using the second method, the sponge was always tipped on to its back as soon as sufficient stones had been removed to allow of manipulating it with ease, leaving the remaining stones to fall out as the sponge was tipped.

The experiment was also tried of hanging the sponge on a wire hook from the top of the aquarium. After a preliminary period of searching, the crab would ascend the wall of the aquarium, cut the sponge round the point where the wire was piercing it so that the sponge fell to the bottom. Then it would descend and replace it on its own back by any one of the recognised methods. The whole operation was usually carried out in a space of 7 minutes.

Finally, if the sponge were removed from a crab's back, placed in the aquarium with a number of other sponges, as well as other materials, the crab, when placed in the aquarium, always selected its own sponge.

CHAPTER THIRTEEN

UBIQUITOUS SNAILS: AND CLOCHE GARDENING

MOST people have marked their first visits to the shore by collecting shells. They are pretty, they are solid and durable. They can be kept without fear of decay or putrefaction ruining our collection or calling down on our heads parental displeasure. They are always attractive in form as well as colour. For some people the pleasure of collecting shells has persisted, or returned, into adult life. It is a short step from collecting shells to wanting to name them, and from there to learning more about the lives of the things that made them. Conchology, the study of shells, early became widespread. Shells readily fossilise and constitute the most abundant and obvious fossils in most sedementary rocks. Altogether, therefore, our knowledge of shells and of the animals that occupied them is about as complete as that of any other group of animals, not excepting birds, the study of which has tended of recent years to overshadow unduly the study of other animals.

The Mollusca, the typically shell-bearing animals, of which there are some 100,000 species, are grouped into five classes. First we have the Gastropods, or univalves, creeping about on a large flattened foot, with one or two pairs of tentacles on the head and, in most species, a spirally-coiled shell. Thomas Pennant, the eighteenth-century contemporary of Gilbert White, referred to them as "Vermes of the soft kind, and simple make, commonly covered with a calcareous habitation". We shall have more to say about their "simple make". Not all the gastropods have shells, or, having them, carry them exposed to view, and the class includes the sea-snails, or periwinkles, and sea-slugs, as well as the land and freshwater snails and the land slugs. In addition, there are the less well-known sea-butterflies.

The next class, the Lamellibranchs, or bivalves, have a shell composed of a right and left valve joined by an elastic hinge. They are represented in the sea by the oysters, mussels, cockles, clams, scallops and ship-worms; and in the fresh water by the swan mussels. The other three classes are the Chitons or coat-of-mail shells, the Elephant-tusk shells, and, finally, the Cephalopods, including the octopus, squid, cuttle, nautilus and argonaut.

The ancestors of all the mollusca lived in the shallow waters of the sea. Some of them, in very early geological times, in the Devonian period, some three hundred million years ago, invaded the land, either by migrating up the beaches and direct on to land, or through the estuaries and into the rivers, and thence on to land. With such a complete fossil record, together with the wide knowledge of the living forms, including in some cases detailed histories of their movements observed over a period of years, it is possible to build up a convincing picture of the fortunes and adventures of the Mollusca as a whole.

All over the world have been found examples of the transition from a marine to a terrestrial habitat by direct migration up the beach, or a transition from a marine to a freshwater habitat. It has been possible to show, for example, that in the tropics, the higher temperatures of the rivers and coastal lakes gives the marine Mollusca a greater tolerance of a lowered salinity, and at many places on the coasts of the Indian Ocean, the Gulf of Mexico and elsewhere, marine species are found in brackish or even completely fresh water. They also furnish an illustration of one of the factors which may have helped the spread from the sea to the river. Thus, in times of drought, with less water coming down the rivers, the estuaries are markedly more saline and marine species can, as a consequence, make their way further up the estuary. Normally such migrations will be temporary, for the period of the drought only, but it only needs a few individuals showing a greater ability to survive in fresh water to become established, to start a permanent migration up the river. Or for a mutation to coincide with these circumstances, producing a mollusc capable of laying resistant eggs or capable of hibernating or resting during a period of intense drought, and the chance of permanent establishment in the new environment and for further migration up the river is increased. Certainly in other instances there are definite indications that the dispersal of molluscs is the result of gradual and random wanderings.

Even the Mollusca now permanently established in fresh water do not differ greatly from those in the littoral zone, and it is clear that once a species has overcome the physiological barrier it spreads rapidly. A very good example is seen in the spread of the so-called Jenkins' spire-shell (*Hydrobia jenkinsi*). Until the end of the nineteenth century, this was confined to the brackish waters of western Europe, including the British Isles. The commencement of its spread was noted and records kept, and it was seen to be making its way inland until now it is abundant in the rivers, streams and canals of England, Wales and Ireland. On the Continent it has also spread rapidly, but there it has kept mainly to the brackish waters.

There is another indication of how a transition from salt to fresh water may occur, from the study of the molluscs of the Baltic region. In the Baltic Sea, the salinity is markedly lower than in the adjacent Atlantic and North Sea waters, and the salinity tends to fall as we pass eastwards. In some places on the eastern shores of the Baltic, the marine cockle and the freshwater snail are found side by side in the same water.

One of the more striking examples of a possible transition from sea to land is found in the characters and zoning of the four species of periwinkles found on our coasts. Indeed, some authorities go so far as to say that these are actually in process of moving from the sea to the land. This can, however, be no more than a matter of opinion. On the other hand, they do show how such a transition could be accomplished and, with variations, probably represent how it has been accomplished in the past.

The first of these is the small periwinkle, the largest individuals of which are barely a quarter of an inch across. Up above mean high-tide mark, lining the cracks in the rocks, it may not be wetted, even by spray, for weeks on end. It feeds on lichens, a land plant, and in its ability to withstand desiccation is almost as much a land animal as the garden snail. Yet it is tied to the sea by its method of reproduction. It spawns into the sea, from September to April, and does so with a fortnightly rhythm, so that the spawning coincides with the periods of the high spring tides, the only times that it is completely submerged by the water. The larvae are free-swimming and spend some time in the sea before settling lower down on the beach, to change into the adult form, after which they move up to the splash zone and remain there for the rest of their lives.

The slightly larger rough periwinkle, white, yellow, brown or black in colour, lives in an equally definite zone further down the shore, from mid-tide level up to the beginning of the splash zone. Less able to resist desiccation than the small periwinkle, it has the advantage that it is viviparous. Fertilisation is internal and the young are born fully formed, covered with a shell. The third species occupies a definite zone also, the zone of the bladder wracks, on which it feeds. It is the obtuse periwinkle, larger than the other two, rounded, yellow, olive-green, brown, black or striped. It lays eggs, in gelatinous masses,

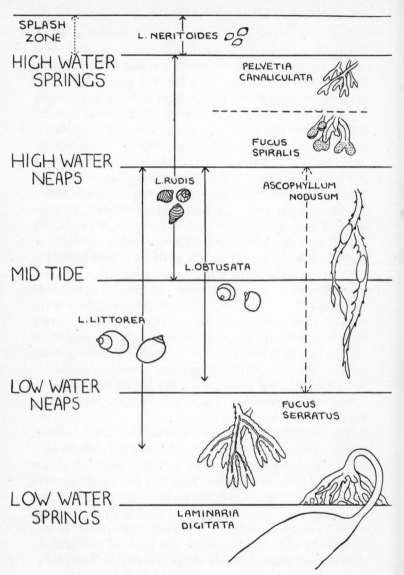

SPLASH
ZONE

L. NERITOIDES

HIGH WATER
SPRINGS

PELVETIA
CANALICULATA

FUCUS
SPIRALIS

HIGH WATER
NEAPS

L.RUDIS

ASCOPHYLLUM
NODUSUM

MID TIDE

L.OBTUSATA

L.LITTOREA

LOW WATER
NEAPS

FUCUS
SERRATUS

LOW WATER
SPRINGS

LAMINARIA
DIGITATA

Some animals and plants of the shore and the zones they occupy.

from which the young are hatched complete with shell. At all stages, however, it needs a damp atmosphere, and for this, as well as for protection from enemies it relies on the seaweed. The fourth species is the common periwinkle, the largest of them all. Black, brown or red in colour, sufficiently familiar to need no further description, it has a much wider vertical range than the other three species, being found from mean low-water springs to about high-water neaps, thus overlapping the range of the obtuse periwinkle. It has, however, a far greater tolerance for widely different types of habitat. It may be found on the bare rocks, on seaweeds, among stones or gravel, on sand or mud. It flourishes equally well on surf-battered coasts and in calm sheltered waters. It is often found well up the estuaries where the water is little more than brackish.

The common periwinkle, like all the gastropods, has a cavity, known as the mantle cavity. Like the obtuse periwinkle, it breathes by means of a gill lodged in that cavity, whereas in the rough and the small periwinkles the gill is reduced in size, the wall of the mantle cavity is plentifully supplied with blood-vessels and is well on the way to becoming a functional lung. At this stage it is not called a lung but a pulmonary cavity, a verbal quibble in effect which tends rather to obscure the true significance of the change that has taken place, for both these species are capable of obtaining oxygen direct from the air. The common periwinkle, regularly exposed at low tide twice a day, would appear capable of using free oxygen also, although it probably relies more on the water enclosed within the mantle cavity from the recent submergence, this being sufficient to tide it over the period of exposure. At all events, these four species give a fairly clear picture of the structural and physiological changes needed to make possible the change from gill-breathing to air-breathing.

The difference between the two forms of breathing is little more than that between two different domestic grates, the one having a good through draught representing the lung and the other, here taken to represent the gill, having a restricted draught. This comparison is not strictly correct, of course, and is used only to stress that the change from the one to the other is relatively simple, as simple as the change from one grate to another. A gill is passive, depending upon the movement of water across it for its oxygen, the lung needing a bellows action for inspiring and exhaling air, together with a more abundant supply of blood-vessels to take in the greater amount of oxygen thus made available.

The common periwinkle has another advantage, which may, partially at least, account for its greater ability to withstand a wide range of environmental conditions. It can adhere to a solid surface, such as a rock or stone, with its muscular foot, and glue the margin of its shell to that surface with a mucus secreted from the foot. In addition, it has an operculum, the thin brown horny disk, known popularly as the winkle head, which effectively seals the entrance to the shell when the animal completely withdraws into it. The periwinkle uses both of these for protection, especially against dessication. Land snails use one or other of these methods, sometimes both, when they withdraw into the shell in dry weather or in winter.

The four species of periwinkles are closely related. So much so that there is very good reason to suppose that they had a common ancestor and that they have diverged from each other in relatively recent times. This cannot be proved beyond a shadow of a doubt but it is a reasonable assumption by comparison with the known history of other species. It is equally reasonable to suppose that a fifth species could arise, by mutation from one of these four, or by hybridisation between two of them. If that species combined the tolerance of a wide range of physical conditions of the common periwinkle, and its ability to seal itself within the shell with an operculum and a gummy mucus, with the internal fertilisation and vivipary of the rough periwinkle and the resistance to desiccation of the small periwinkle, the ability to live completely on land would be almost if not wholly complete.

It is particularly apt that this example should be available to us for the periwinkles, like the great majority of gastropods, are fairly generalised. Recalling our example of the wardrobe, it means that they are potentially capable of occupying a wide variety of situations with little or no change. Pennant, as we have seen, described them as "of simple structure", which merely expresses the same idea, whether that was what he intended by his remark or not. It is relevant to recall that of the five classes of molluscs, two only have penetrated into the fresh waters, the bivalves and the gastropods, and only one, the gastropods, the most generalised of all, have emerged on to the land.

The generalised form of the gastropods is worth further consideration. The likelihood is that they are the most primitive of all molluscs, although opinion may not be unanimous on this, for the coat-of-mail shells are sometimes quoted as the most primitive of living molluscs. Nevertheless, the gastropods are found in the earliest fossil-bearing rocks. A general consideration of their form and their structure suggests that they must be very close to the ancestors of all molluscs; and, taking it all in all, they have deviated little from a generalised plan throughout their long geological history. Moreover, and again generally speaking, there is a close similarity between the sea-snails and the sea-slugs, on the one hand, and the land snails and land slugs, on the other. Added to this, those gastropods living on land show a remarkable adaptability to varying conditions, and an ability to occupy a wide variety of ecological niches without showing a very wide range of change in structure, of the body or the shell.

Perhaps the generalised nature of the gastropods is best emphasised by examining the specialisation found in other groups of molluscs, and by tabulating the reasons why they have been prevented from following the gastropods up the beaches or up the rivers and on to dry land.

The oyster has on occasion been quoted as the epitome of an inert existence. As a larva it is free-living and capable of a limited locomotion; but once the spat has fallen and anchored itself the oyster is fixed to one spot. It has sacrificed the power of locomotion and specialised in a method of drawing through its two valves a current of water, bringing to it oxygen for respiration and food in the form of microscopic plants and animals. Colaterally, by this fixed and solitary existence it has been restricted in its reproduction to a random spawning, shedding its germ-cells into the sea in large number to take their chance of survival. More or less, the same is true of all bivalves. Mussels are little better, although a laborious progression can be made by using the threads of the beard, or byssus. Others, like the cockles are slightly better off, being able to burrow into sand with the aid of a muscular foot, or even to progress by leaps with the aid of that same organ. Scallops can swim by the alternate opening and shutting of the valves, but, even so, to label this very restricted method of moving about as "swimming" is rather to overstate the case. Some clams and others like the razor-shells can also burrow and do so with a remarkable celerity. But all have specialised in a particular method of feeding, by drawing water through the shell and across the body, to take the crumbs, so to speak. In doing so they have been compelled to retain the primitive method of reproduction, which, linked with other things, has made emergence on land impossible, although a few species have made their way into the fresh waters.

The specialisation seen in the bivalves has led to what we should normally call a degeneration, although this word, in biological parlance, has little real meaning. It is axiomatic that evolution is not necessarily synonymous with progress. Moreover, it becomes almost impossible to define progress in a biological sense. The bivalves have evolved, or progressed, or specialised, along one line and have stood still along others. Yet they are successful, as witness their persistence in time. They have progressed along a special line of feeding, they have stood still in the matter of reproduction, their random spawning being no better than that used by sponges, sea-anemones and other of the lower animals; and they have gone back, relatively to most other mollusca, in so far as they have lost their heads. In many cases, as in the oyster, the foot is no longer functional as an organ of locomotion in the adult.

A similar uneven development of organs or general functioning is seen in that other large group of molluscs, the cephalopods, which, judged by human rather than biological standards, have been highly successful. In the squid, octopus and cuttle, that part of the body corresponding to the foot in the gastropods has become highly specialised to form a head with a ring of very elaborate tentacles, used for the capture of food and only secondarily as a means of locomotion. With this elaboration of the head region has come a highly efficient eye which structurally compares closely with that of the vertebrates. The brain, too, is more elaborate than that of other molluscs, giving it a higher capacity for learning by experience, and an elaboration of behaviour generally to give an appearance almost of intelligence. In many other aspects of its behaviour, also, it bears comparison, certainly with the higher invertebrates, such as insects, and even with some of the lower vertebrates. This is especially well shown in its courtship behaviour. Indeed, from many points of view, the cephalopods early in their geological history developed many of the traits which would have made an emergence on land possible. Yet they have failed to colonise even the fresh waters. As to their failure to colonise the land, the reason can be seen in two things, which are closely linked: their primary method of locomotion is by a water-jet propulsion, this is the line along which they have specialised. This method of locomotion is linked with a respiration by means of gills which is dependent also upon the water drawn into the mantle cavity.

Perhaps a more striking example of extreme specialisation, giving by its great contrast a striking illustration of the advantage to the gastropods of their generalised organisation, is found in the giant clam, a bivalve mollusc. Fortunately, this has been subject in recent years to a close study by Professor C. M. Yonge.

Land animals living in the tropics counter the intense heat of the sun in a variety of ways. Elephants seek the shade of trees; hippopotamuses, even tigers, prefer to spend the period of midday heat in water. Truly desert animals, like the jerboas and desert rats, where there is little cover or water, stay underground during the day, coming out at night, or are physically so constructed that an atmosphere of extreme heat or extreme dryness can be countered by natural mechanical means. The camel is a typical example of this last. The irregular shape of the body, the long neck and legs, permit the maximum loss of body heat, and although it does not store water in its stomach, as is popularly supposed, it can conserve water. This much is obvious even although we do not yet know precisely how it is accomplished. Land animals, then, avoid the full effects of heat and dryness, and do so either by their behaviour or by their physical structure. Indeed there is no other way they could do so.

As we have seen, one of the most striking features of the animals living between tide-marks on our own coasts is the behavioural trick or the structural device for keeping cool and moist. The tropical strand should show this even more clearly. Yet there are certain shore animals that actually bask in the intense sunlight, and the most remarkable of these are the giant clams of the Indo-Pacific.

One of the most conspicuous things on certain coral reefs are these large clams, up to four and a half feet long, standing three feet high and having a gape of two feet across, their total weight sometimes as much as six hundredweight. At extreme low-tide their boulder-like masses stand up fully exposed, planted on the substratum where the two halves of the massive shell are joined by a hinge. The more ordinary shellfish of our temperate coasts close as the water recedes. They close also when covered by no more than a few inches of water. But the giant clams do exactly the opposite. They gape to the full when covered

The giant clam of tropical seas exposing a broad surface to the sun at low-tide.

by a foot or less of water, heated to a temperature of 30 degrees Centigrade, or when fully exposed to the direct glare of the sun.

There is another difference between the common or garden shellfish and the giant clams. When the former gape, they expose a cavity. Lining the inside of each half of the shell, each valve as it is called, is a layer of flesh, the mantle. The space between the two halves of the mantle is partly occupied by the body proper of the mollusc, the fleshy part of which is known as the foot. Anyone who has opened an oyster, mussel or cockle can picture this sufficiently for our present purpose. Lying at one end of the body in the cockle, say, is a pair of short tubes, the siphons. It is through one of these that water is drawn in, passed across the gills, and out again through the other tube. This stream of water brings in food and oxygen, for feeding and breathing, and in passing out takes with it the waste matter from the body of the shellfish.

This lengthy explanation is necessary since without it we cannot appreciate the remarkable changes that have taken place in the clam's body. The giant clam is related to the cockle, although putting the two side by side it is difficult to believe this. Not only is there the great difference in size, but the cockle burrows in the sand, using its fleshy foot as a kind of probe and spade combined, whereas the giant clam is perched on the surface. Of all the differences between them, however, the most striking is the appearance of the gape. In the largest of the giant clams, the space between the edges of the two colossal valves is entirely filled with a mass of flesh, with two openings, the mouths of the siphons, set wide apart from each other. This expanse of flesh is beautifully coloured, with yellow, red, purple and green.

If the cockle and the giant clam are so very different in appearance and habits, it has been brought about by what is, in fact, a very simple alteration in the anatomy. At some time in the past history of the giant clam, the hinge between the valves has migrated through 180 degrees. No doubt this, together with all the accompanying changes came about by easy stages, but they gave us the first attempt at cloche-gardening.

As the hinge migrated, other parts of the mollusc moved with it. Notably, one siphon followed it round, at least part of the way, while the other moved but little. The small amount of flesh lying between the pair of siphons as seen in the cockle, became much enlarged, broadened and lengthened and very fleshy, to fill almost completely the gap between the edges of the valves.

Had these been the only changes we should have had a clam differing from the cockle in appearance only and one moreover conferring distinct disadvantages on its possessor. As it is, instead of disadvantages, we have an animal capable of growing to giant size, of living and thriving under the adverse conditions of the inter-tidal zone. All

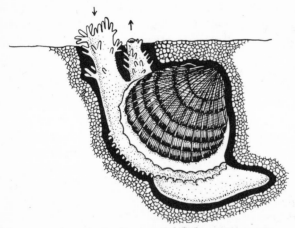

A cockle showing the plough-shaped foot, used in burrowing, and the siphons through which water is drawn in and driven out of the body.

this has been accomplished by the addition of a few simple accessory changes. The giant clams, of which there are several species, including the six-hundredweight colossus, are the sole shellfish, except for one other, of a different family, living in the Pacific, that have gone in for horticulture on a wide scale. In the surface layers of the mass of flesh lying between the two siphons live thousands of microscopic unicellular plants, or algae. They are guests of the clam, paying guests, as we shall see.

Plants differ from animals in a number of important

ways. They can manufacture their own food with the aid of sunshine; and the more sunshine they have, everything else being equal, the better they thrive. Also in the course of using the sun's rays for the manufacture of starches and later sugars, a quantity of surplus oxygen is produced. Plants, then, need as much sun as possible; marine animals cannot stand more than the barest minimum of it. Plants give off oxygen under the influence of the sun; marine animals like all others need oxygen; in fact, on a crowded coral reef there is keen competition for the available supply. Plants manufacture their own food; animals must take it from the plants. As between the microscopic plants and the giant clam, it is almost a case of Jack Spratt and his wife, what the one does not want the other needs.

The microscopic plants are not so much guests, perhaps, as prisoners of the clam. Each is imprisoned within one of the cells in the tissues of the clam. For a while it feeds, manufactures oxygen, some of which is used by the clam, and reproduces itself by dividing in two. Every now and then a cell in the clam tissues, one containing an alga, will migrate inwards towards the clam's stomach. There the alga will be digested.

The relationship between the clam and its alga-guests, or prisoners, is in principle precisely that existing between man and his lettuces, or any other green vegetable. Furthermore, when man prides himself on having invented cloche gardening, he is several million years behind hand, for we may take it for granted that the changes which converted a cockle into a giant clam took a very long time. One of these produced the first cloches, for spaced throughout the skin of the clam are a number of flask-shaped lenses, transparent living lenses, and around these the one-called plants are clustered. The lenses concentrate the sun's rays on the plants, thus increasing their rate of growth, or, to use the familiar gardening term, forcing them.

The giant clam, thanks to comparatively trivial structural changes and to a symbiosis, or living together, with minute and otherwise insignificant plants, has become highly specialised. Unlike the general run of shore animals it can face up to the rigours of the inter-tidal zone and, in defiance of them, thrive exceedingly. It feeds, like a cockle, on minute particles drawn in through its siphons. It breathes like a cockle, on oxygen carried in the water drawn in through the siphons. In addition, it feeds on its own domesticated plants, as well as using the oxygen its kitchen gardens give off. Thus, we can understand how, under the most adverse circumstances, it can grow to a giant size.

What we have not explained is how it can withstand the very high temperatures. We must leave this for future investigators and content ourselves with recalling that there are animals capable of living all their lives in the boiling water of hot springs, or in petroleum springs. The protoplasm of no two animals is alike in its fads and fancies, or in the conditions it can stand up to. This, true for individuals, is even more true as we pass from one species to another. It is just one more of the many things that have had their influence on the changes wrought through the ages in living organisms, and not least in that sifting process that determines which animals shall stay in the sea and which shall be able to emerge successfully on to dry land.

CHAPTER FOURTEEN

MUSEUM OF MAN'S ANCESTRY

UP to this point we have been dealing only with invertebrates. We have seen how a minority of groups, the Echinoderms being outstanding, have failed to penetrate even the fresh waters let alone emerge on to dry land. Others, such as sponges, coelenterates and one group of molluscs have managed to colonise the rivers and lakes. Yet other groups, such as the annelid worms, the crustacea and the gastropod molluscs have sent outliers into the fresh waters, even on to land, while the bulk of their members are still marine. Of the remaining main groups of invertebrates, the insects and the spiders, all we can say in such a brief summary is that they have so completely taken to the land, with some members inhabiting fresh water, and even fewer having made secondarily a return to the sea, that if our knowledge depended on the study alone of their living representatives, it would be difficult to believe that they or their ancestors were ever marine.

We can look at this another way: that as we pass in review from the most primitive to the more highly specialised invertebrates, we see, broadly speaking, a greater and greater tendency to leave the salt water and travel either up the beaches and through the rivers on to land. Then, when we come to the most highly organised of all invertebrates, the insects and the spiders, we have only the slightest evidence, from the geological record, as well as from the structure and habits of their members now living, that they ever had anything to do with the sea, so complete is their severance from the sea both now and since early geological times. So we are faced with a perplexity. On the one hand, the more one learns of the animal kingdom as a whole the more one is impressed with a picture in which the goal of evolution seems to be to get on to land. It seems very certain that life originated in the shallow seas. All the evidence goes to show that the inter-tidal zone formed and probably still forms a testing ground for new adaptations, leading to a greater and greater ability to be independent of the sea as a means of livelihood. And to return to the analogy of the steeplechase, we can see why some have failed at the fence, why others have just managed to get over it and go no further. What we are at such difficulty to see is how the others, galloping away to the winning post, the insects and the majority of the vertebrates managed to clear the fence and get so far ahead of all the rest.

For convenience we will ignore the insects and give our attention solely to the vertebrates, for it is on their fortunes that my early remark—that if the moon had not become separated from the earth man would not have come into being—is to be justified or refuted. There is, of course, one ready answer which should not be ignored: that this whole idea of an evolutionary emergence from sea to land is a scientist's illusion; that to sustain this thesis he unconsciously—some people even suggest maliciously—bends the evidence to support a pre-conceived idea. Or even that he selects, for whatever motive, only that evidence which suits his purpose while suppressing all other. It is not possible fully to argue this in so short a space, just as it is not possible to present all the minutiae of the evidence upon which the theory of organic evolution is now based. All one can say is that every fresh piece of evidence, from whatever source it is derived, and from whatever angle it is examined, fits into and supports the general picture of a transition from sea to land. That there are tremendous gaps in our knowledge no one will deny. That there are anomalies is equally certain. That scientists have made errors, and will continue to do so is beyond a doubt. Yet in spite of such errors the story of evolution still carries conviction. Indeed, as soon as an error is corrected it is seen that the truth supports the story far more than the error detracted from it. To carry this theme further will be to lose sight of the thread of our present discussion. It was entered upon solely because when we come to the vertebrates, as we must next, we find what is probably the biggest gap of all in our knowledge.

Before passing to the vertebrates, however, I should like to refer briefly to another offshoot of our discussion. I shall initiate this by referring to something that happened to a former neighbour of mine. He had an apple tree loaded with fruit, so loaded in fact that when it was all gathered his greatest problem was what should be done with it so that it should not go to waste. Long before he had finished picking the fruit this problem was apparent to him. Yet there came the moment when all the apples were gathered except for one small solitary apple at the extreme tip of a slender branch that rose straight up to form by far the highest point of the tree. To use his own words, he could not leave that one apple, although he was burdened with a glut of apples, and risked life and limb in striving upwards to pick it. Being something of a philosopher he added that, to him, this seemed to epitomise human behaviour.

It may be, of course, that this is a fantasy of the human mind, this idea of striving ever higher and higher. Yet certain people could not rest until Mount Everest, the highest point on land had been reached. There are others who seek to fly to the moon. Our aeroplanes are for ever striving to gain more and more altitude records. We thrust our buildings ever higher into the sky. Materially and morally, as well as spiritually, human beings are striving upwards. If there is any one lesson more certain than another from our findings in the biological field, it is that human behaviour derives from common springs with that of the rest of the animal kingdom, flows along the same line and bears comparison qualitatively if not quantitatively.

The emergence from the sea on to the land seems to have this same quality, of an inherent striving upwards. This may be, and probably is, completely delusory. It is, in fact, possible to give the more prosaic explanation that the struggle for existence, the competition for food and living space, was bound to force a migration on to the land as soon as the necessary structures and adaptations appeared. That this migration is no more than an impelled search for fresh pastures, an impulse to occupy vacant ecological niches, in the same way as there has been a migration from the shallow seas in to the deeper seas, even to the uttermost depths of the ocean. This seems reasonable enough until we learn that the migration on to the land was already accomplished by the invertebrates during the Devonian period, 300 million years ago, and, according to one eminent palaeontologist at least, the deep seas were not invaded until some 150 million years later, at a time when there were already well-advanced reptiles living on land many of them living under desert conditions. It may be that there will emerge in the future a full and satisfactory explanation of this, but at the moment it is perplexing to understand why this should have been so when the greater changes were necessary for the transition of the purely aquatic to the purely terrestrial way of life.

So much then for idle and probably wholly fanciful speculation. At least this digression has drawn attention to one thing essential to the continuance of our story, namely, that to look for the origin of the land vertebrates we must go a long way back in time. And this alone explains why there is so little fossil evidence to bridge the very wide gap between the simplest vertebrates and the invertebrates.

First, let us examine this gap to see exactly what it comprises. Later we can see what evidence we have with which to bridge it. As for the gap, on the one hand we have the invertebrates, a miscellaneous crowd of animals having superficially little in common with each other. Yet they are capable of being so arranged that they present a fairly continuous series showing an increasing complexity, in which the successive transitional steps are moderately well represented. We start with the unicellular animals, in which all the processes of life are carried on within a single unit of protoplasm contained within a single cell-wall and controlled by a central nucleus. Some people prefer to call them non-cellular, thus emphasising that in none is the protoplasm simple and in certain of them it is a complex of structures corresponding to the organs of higher animals but without cell-walls bounding them. Then we have the sponges, with bodies of many cells, with tissues of simple architecture, an internal skeleton of mainly isolated units (the spicules), and capable of being dissociated into their component cells, which then for a time behave like unicellular animals. They have, however, little or no muscle tissues and only the very beginning of nerve-cells at the most, and no sense-organs.

From the sponges we pass through the coelenterates, the sea-anemones, hydroids and jellyfishes, skirt the aberrant echinoderms (starfishes, sea-urchins and sea-cucumbers) in which muscles become more and more in evidence. The scattered nerve-cells give way to a nerve-net and finally real nerves, associated with sense-organs of a simple type. And the skeleton, if present, is laid down in the outer tissues so that it encloses the body more or less. So we come to the Annelid worms, with the body made up of rings or segments actuated by successive series of muscle-groups, and by long muscles passing the length of the body. The digestive system is a long tube passing the length of the body, from the mouth in front to the anus in the rear. The nervous system is now a longitudinal cord giving off slender branches or nerves to the separate organs. The skeleton, where recognisable, is external to the body. And sense-organs, while still very simple, are becoming more clearly recognisable.

All the things found in the worms are carried forward, with increasingly complex organisation, through the mollusca to the insects and spiders, and in these, in spite of the increases in the complexity of the bodily structure, the skeleton is still external, and the nerve cord is still underneath the digestive tube or gut. The full picture is by no means as simple as it is drawn here; nor is the progression from the one to the other as clear-cut as this summary would lead one to suppose. There are exceptions and apparent contradictions, minor gaps in the sequence and perplexing divergences all along the line. Even so, there is a continuum, an underlying theme, recognisable in the diversity as much as the underlying theme by Corelli can be recognised in Kreisler's variations on it. Above all, there is an undoubted similarity in behaviour, of the individual cells and their components as well as in the gross behaviour of the individual animals themselves. So we are justified in the concept of the typical invertebrate as a simple animal characterised more especially by an external skeleton and a nerve-cord lying beneath the gut.

The vertebrates constitute a more homogeneous group, which may be described, briefly, as characterised by an internal skeleton and a nerve cord lying above the gut. The muscle system is far more complicated, the nervous system more highly developed, including especially the brain, and altogether the vertebrates are markedly more complex in the architecture of the body. Superficially, they are worlds apart from the invertebrates, and yet we find similarities with them in the behaviour of the component cells, in the internal behaviour of these cells and also in the gross behaviour of the individuals themselves, which leave little doubt that invertebrates and vertebrates alike are one in flesh and origin. In the past there have been several painstaking and lengthy attempts to explain this apparently deep gulf between them in their structure, none of which has been particularly satisfactory. This was largely because the writers of these bulky tomes concentrated on trying to explain how a nerve cord lying under the gut could have come to lie above it, and how an external skeleton could have been replaced by one that was internal. Above all, the writers were trying to derive the first vertebrates in a direct line of succession from the higher invertebrates.

The geological succession of life shows us that in the first fossil-bearing rocks, the Cambrian, all the main groups of invertebrates were already in being. Twenty million years later, a short space of time as geological time goes, the first forerunner of the vertebrates is met, in the Ordovician, the fossil known as *Jamoytius*. This, together with other evidence, justifies us in the assumption that early in time, at what point we cannot yet be sure, nor in what manner, the main vertebrate stock diverged from the main invertebrate stock, from an ancestral form of relatively simple construction. Thereafter each pursued its separate line of development. If this be true, then the remarkable thing is not that they show wide differences, as in the position of the nerve cord, but that they should show such astonishing similarities and especially in the detail of their behaviour.

Before going further into this, it is necessary to set at rest a conflict of names. We speak of vertebrates, in contradistinction to invertebrates as though there were two main groups in the animal kingdom, those with backbones and those without backbones. It is a usage that started with the early days of organised zoology, and it is a convenience to continue it for everyday purposes because it gives a concept which is clear and understandable even to those with the most limited knowledge of the subject. This very simplicity in names brings with it, however, an obstacle to further understanding, in so far as it implants the idea that all animals can be placed in one or other of two separate compartments, as distinct from each other as the contents of two wooden boxes. To explore the position more fully we have to introduce the more explicit division into invertebrates and chordates.

The internal skeleton of the so-called vertebrates consists of a backbone, the main support and strut, to which are attached limb-bones, a thoracic basket formed of the ribs and breastbone for the protection of the lungs, and a skull or cranium for housing the brain. In the development of the embryo, the backbone is first laid down as a stiff rod, the notochord. As development proceeds this is strengthened with bone, or cartilage in some cases, and becomes divided into segments, forming what are known as vertebrae, from which processes grow up to enclose the main nerve cord, or spinal cord. Essentially, the foundation of the backbone, so characteristic of the higher animals which we have accustomed ourselves to calling the vertebrates, is a rod of tissue known as the notochord. In the sharks and rays it becomes sheathed in cartilage, and these fishes are sometimes referred to, as a consequence, as the cartilaginous fishes. In all other fishes, in the amphibia, reptiles, birds and mammals, the notochord is replaced by bone. In the lampreys and hagfishes, eel-like and fish-like in appearance, except that they have no jaws, the notochord persists throughout life and is the sole support running the length of the body. It serves no doubt to prevent a shortening of the body when the muscles contract and no more. All these groups, including the lampreys and hagfishes must be referred to as chordates, animals with a notochord. Then we can begin to interpret the earliest known remains of fish-like creatures, the early fossil known as *Jamoytius*, and also those now living, such as Amphioxus, the sea-squirts and the acorn-barnacles. Through them, the gap between the invertebrates on the one hand and the land vertebrates on the other can be considerably narrowed.

If the main line of chordate evolution be likened to a rope, then the connecting links afforded by the proto-chordates (the early chordates such as *Jamoytius*, Amphi-oxus and the sea-squirts) appear as the loose strands where the rope has parted. In the geological succession we start with a simple fish-like form, *Jamoytius*, with continuous fins, without jaws, and with a cartilaginous skeleton little better than the simple notochord. Its remains were found in the estuarine shales of the late Silurian. In the rocks of

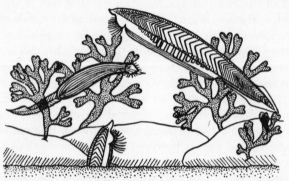

Amphioxus, the lancelet, living in the sand of the shore recalls the remote ancestors of man.

this same period are found the remains of the Ostraco-derms, comparable with the present-day lampreys, and occasional fragments of true fishes. In the next period, the Devonian, the lamprey-like Ostracoderms have become more abundant, to be followed later in the period by numerous true fishes, and, incidentally, by Amphibia in late Devonian times. There is therefore the appearance of a succession from a simple protochordate to a true verte-brate, even to one living partially on land, within the comparatively short space of fifty million years. Colaterally with this, we have the fact that in the development of each individual vertebrate, the notochord appears first, to be later replaced by a backbone. The scientist may be forgiven if he sees in this more than a coincidence and interprets it as a sign that the individual is telling us through its early development what took place in the evolution of its own ancestors. Then, to support this view he finds in the shallow seas to-day, even on the beach where anyone may go and look for himself, animals now living which can be placed in a series to represent these same steps.

The scientist who is not so bothered by superficial appearances, who examines the inner structure and weighs the evidence of biological processes, sees nothing remarkable in the idea that the invertebrates and the vertebrates have had a common ancestry. The sceptics are found more especially among those who are influenced by superficial appearances, who look at a dog, say, or a horse, or even at man himself, and say it is absurd to suppose they have anything in common with a worm or an insect. It is precisely here that the protochordates have a value, for while having the inner structure of the more typical chordate or vertebrate (it is difficult to avoid the use of this familiar word) they have the external appearance more of the typical invertebrate. The Amphioxus, or lancelet is perhaps the least like an invertebrate, except in its habits. Two or three inches long, it has a somewhat fish-like body, tapering to a point at each end, with continuous fins, like the Silurian *Jamoytius*. It is yellowish in colour and lives by burrowing in the sand. Lying buried except for its front end—there is no recognisable head—it strains the water for small organisms or particles through a circlet of small tentacles fringing the mouth. Fish-like, perhaps, yet suggestive of a worm in general appearance, it has a well developed musculature, comparable with that of a true vertebrate, a nerve cord lying over the gut, and above all this well-formed notochord. Occasionally it may be found between tide-marks, at the very low spring tides, but it belongs more strictly to the shallow offshore waters.

The sea-squirts on the other hand, are found in great abundance between tide-marks, as well as in deeper waters; and they also have relatives that live in the very great depths and others that drift in the surface waters. These last could easily be mistaken for some peculiar form of jellyfish, as indeed could those fixed to the rocks between tide-marks, although others, of a more flattened

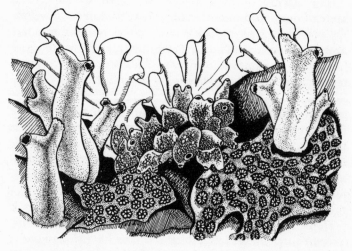

Large solitary sea-squirts and related colonial forms encrusting the rocks.

form on the inter-tidal rocks and seaweeds are often mistaken for sponges even by experienced zoologists. Their inelegant name derives from the habit of contracting suddenly if touched and ejecting a jet of water. They live by drawing water through an opening in the jelly-like sac of a body, passing it across a complicated set of gills, at the same time extracting any food particles it contains, and ejecting the water through another opening on the body. The adult sea-squirt is sans eyes, sans nose, sans everything that could link it with the typical vertebrates. Its nervous system is reduced almost to vanishing point, its musculature is simple and it has no skeleton of any kind. The interest, therefore, lies more in its larva, which looks like a minute tadpole. And in the tail of this tadpole is a notochord. There is no alternative to seeing in the sea-squirt an early chordate that has reverted in the adult to the appearance and habits of an invertebrate—if reverted is not too strong a word—but which betrays in its early life history an affinity with the vertebrates.

There are a number of other animals, some even more problematic than the sea-squirt, all of which contribute some small shred of evidence to the frayed strands of the vertebrate rope. One other only need be cited. This the acorn-worm, also burrowing in the sand in the shallow waters, seldom between tide-marks. It lives in a U-shaped burrow, very much in the manner of the lugworm, has gills comparable in structure to those of the lancelet, a nervous system like that of a starfish, has the remains of a notochord, and has a larva very like the peculiar larvae of starfishes and sea-urchins. It has, however, no skeleton apart from the small structure which has been interpreted as the remains of a notochord.

If we are to interpret the lancelet, sea-squirts and acorn-worms as representatives of the various stages that led to the evolution of the vertebrates, it may well be asked why they have not been found fossil, and why if they are so archaic have they persisted until to-day. To the first of these the reply can be made that they have no hard skeleton to make their preservation as fossils likely. Even so, fossil evidence may yet come to light. *Jamoytius*, which is in similar case, only came to light in 1946 when Dr Errol White hit upon a new way of examining a piece of shale that had been collected many years before. As to why these archaic forms have persisted, we can point to the lamp-shell, *Lingula*, which has persisted almost unchanged since the Ordovician period, for a period of over 300 million years and is still sufficiently plentiful on the shores of Japan, Indonesia and elsewhere to be used in some places as food. We are so sure of its history because it has a horny shell which preserves well.

We also have the persistence of the lungfishes, capable of breathing air, now restricted to rivers of Australia, West Africa and South America. And mention of these takes us naturally on to our next point. In the Devonian rocks are found the remains of three main groups of fishes. The first, the Osteolepids, died out in the Permian period, some 200 million years later. The second group is that of the Coelacanths, and the third is the Dipnoi, or lungfishes.

The simple tadpole of a sea-squirt is active and free-swimming.

The latter still persists, as we have just seen, in Australia, West Africa and South America. The Coelacanths were believed to have died out 50 million years ago until, in 1938, a Coelacanth was caught off the coast of South Africa, to be followed by another in 1952 caught in that same area of the globe.

There is a general impression, fostered by statements made in popular books on the subject, that the swim-bladder of fishes, the "silver-gut" as it is sometimes called, and which is exposed as a long thin silvery bladder when certain food-fishes are opened up, is the forerunner of the lung of the lungfishes, and therefore of the lung of terrestrial vertebrates. The truth seems to be otherwise, although it must be confessed that the problem of the swim-bladder and its relation to the lung of air-breathing verte-brates is a long way from being solved. Whether the lung first appeared as a hydrostatic swim-bladder, used for regulating the vertical movements of a fish, or whether it originated as a true lung which was later converted into a hydrostatic organ by being closed to the exterior, is not known. The fossil evidence is insufficient to solve it and opinion on it is divided. All we have is the fact that most bony fishes to-day have a swim-bladder, that lungs are present in the lungfishes, that the sharks and rays, primitive fishes, of more ancient design than the bony fishes, have neither.

In deriving the land vertebrates from these early fishes, we have the supporting evidence of the Amphibia, which geologically speaking, followed closely the earliest lung-fishes. This is especially so in the life-history of the frog, wherein the tadpole is aquatic and fish-like and later loses its tail, develops lungs and four limbs and come to live mainly on land. The evidence, much too extensive to be given here in any sort of detail, points to the possibility of ancestral fishes, having lungs, coming up the rivers and by a series of structural changes, giving rise to descendants capable of living partly on land and partly in the water. These we suppose to have been the forerunners of the amphibia and the reptiles, and through them of the birds and mammals. The real course of these changes is, for our present purpose, not of particular importance. It is suffi-cient that the signs we can draw from both extinct and living fishes support the thesis that the shallow waters and especially the inter-tidal conditions must have contributed to their evolution into land-breathing vertebrates.

Merely to take a few items at random, we can point to the number of inter-tidal fishes that have developed some form of parental care. This may take the form of the con-struction of a nest, as in the stickleback, or the depositing of the eggs in masses in the crevice of a rock, under stones or in empty shells, as with gobies, blennies, bullheads and clingfishes. Or it may be the brooding of the eggs as in lumpsuckers and butterfishes. This attention to the welfare of the offspring is in contrast to the random spawning of the more sea-going fishes such as mackerel and herring, and represents the development of a tendency towards a parental care which was a necessary prerequisite to life on land. As to respiration and locomotion, there is the example of the mud-skipper of the tropics, which is able to leave the water for long periods, and, using its fins partially as limbs, move about on land.

In fishes, therefore, in both extinct and in living species, and first in one species and then in another, we see present or developing all the requisites for the transition from an aquatic to a terrestrial life. Above all, and probably the one decisive feature, although its importance is not usually stressed sufficiently, there is the development of true jaws, seen for the first time in the early fishes. This made generalised feeding on land possible and must have had a particular significance, other things being already present, in the mass conquest of the land.

CHAPTER FIFTEEN

POSTSCRIPT

IN December, 1952, the dramatic news was flashed across the world that a second Coelacanth fish had been caught, the first having been obtained in 1938 at about the same time of the year. For a while, the fish was the subject of broadcasts, it was given prominent space in the newspapers and in all manner of journals. It was NEWS. Why? Some scientists told us its capture was important because it would shed fresh light on man's ancestry. Others seemed less sure of this. The truth is that no single discovery of this sort ever sheds more than a small quota of light on the general problem of man's ancestry or on the greater problem of evolution as a whole. At best it enables us to fit one or two more pieces into the jigsaw. As to the interest aroused by the capture of the Coelacanth, we cannot suppose that the average man is so thirsty for knowledge of his remote ancestors. Rather it was a case of the lost talent of silver. The Coelacanths were believed to have become extinct fifty million years ago and, behold, one of them believed lost for ever is still found to be with us. In any case, even if this highly interesting survivor has a story to tell it will be years before the examination of it is completed and a correct assessment made. The building up of scientific evidence is a slow and laborious process, and it is as well to emphasise this.

One cannot help contrasting the widespread interest in the Coelacanth with that taken in other equally illuminating beasts. It is doubtful, for example, if any editor would accept an article on the sea-squirt, even although it had shed light on man's ancestry. As for the lancelet, the treasured object of the biologist, it forms almost the staple food of the people living on the coast of Amoy, in China, where it is fished by the ton each year. The lampshell, *Lingula*, which has come down to us almost unchanged for 300 million years, is eaten in Indonesia, while the king-crab, a survival from 250 million years ago, is fished off the Atlantic coast of the U.S.A., its eggs used for chicken feed. And, after all, every shark is a survivor of an extremely archaic race, older even than the Coelacanth, and there is no need to describe what everyone, and especially the ocean-going seamen, think of sharks.

A fish that came to life after being thought extinct for millions of years: the Coelacanth.

On the whole, there is little chance of anything spectacular appearing to add considerably to the story of evolution as it is now known. The evidence we have is founded upon the close study of a wide range of living animals as well as on the study of a multitude of fossils. New species of animals are being discovered every year, many of them taken from the sea. For the most part they do no more than fill in the minute interstices in the framework of the story. Occasionally, a new approach is provided by renewed study of some form already well known, and it is in this field that the more fruitful results are to be expected. Such a new approach has already been reached, through the observations made on the inherent rhythmic activity, and, in my opinion, it is one of the more important, if unspectacular, discoveries of recent years.

If, now, we can recapitulate the discussion elaborated in the preceding chapters we have the following. The evidence, fossil and recent, suggests that life began in the shallow waters of the seas and that its early unfolding took place there. In time there came an invasion of the land and, at a later date, a similar but less abundant and less spectacular invasion of the deep seas took place. This in itself is remarkable, that the main evolutionary surge should have been, not into the relative calm of the stable environment of the deep seas but on to land, where conditions are so much more variable and rigorous. The key to all this lies, of course, in the dependence of all living matter on the energy derived from the sun. The first to come ashore must have been the plants. That follows as a matter of course. These would be succeeded—they may even have been accompanied—by animals feeding on them. Nevertheless, there can be little doubt that the rigours of the inter-tidal zone offered those conditions for apprenticeship necessary to the successful invasion of the land, whether by plants or by animals.

So far as the terrestrial animals now living are concerned, we can recognise, broadly, two groups. First, there are those living under conditions which, in principle, differ only slightly from those on the shore. These include such things as earthworms, slugs, snails and woodlice, which can survive only under conditions that are sub-aquatic. They are still dependent upon a humid atmosphere and readily suffer from desiccation. This is true even of the desert snails. Their invasion might almost be described as passive, an invasion that was only possible and which must be continually supported by physical conditions that are only slightly removed from the ancestral marine conditions. The second group, by far the largest, includes those animals capable of living independently of a humid atmosphere. This is, obviously, only relative and in any case there is a marked dependence upon water taken internally. Even so, there is a greater freedom of action and movement, and an ability to move into dry places provided water is available for periodic drinking.

The necessary conditions for life on land, most marked in the second group may be summarised as follows. Clearly, the first requisite is some form of active locomotion throughout life. Secondly, a well-developed skeleton becomes necessary to support a body which, under aquatic conditions, would be supported by pressure from the surrounding water. An external skeleton, as in insects, is adequate but it places a limit on the size of the individual. The genesis of an internal skeleton was, therefore, a prerequisite to the maintenance of size with the emergence from a supporting aquatic medium to the unsupported life on land or in air. Thirdly, the mechanism for resisting desiccation must be evolved, together with different methods of breathing. Fourthly, there must be protection for the germ-cells during what may be broadly called the period of fertilization, as well as for the offspring arising from them. These have been met by a greater development of shelled eggs, or by internal fertilization, and there is the greater need in either case for an increase in parental care.

The development of an active means of locomotion brought its own peculiar results. It made possible a complete differentiation into separate sexes without endangering the future of the race. If sedentary organisms were separated into males and females, the chances of their germ-cells meeting would be slender. It would be still possible, although hazardous, under aquatic conditions; it would be impossible on land. Active locomotion demands also a more highly-organised musculature. This in turn needs a more highly developed nervous system to actuate the muscles, a better system of blood supply to feed them and a greater need for food. So unsupported movement on land or in the air calls for a greater and more constant supply of energy. This would not be possible except in an environment populated by abundant organisms, the plants, capable of manufacturing food from the elements with the aid of the sun's rays. The emergence of plants into the full glare of the sun not only made their greater development possible but ensured the necessary supplies of food for the energy-consuming land animals which followed. On land, also, the greater direct use of the sun-rays by irradiation of the tissues provides a subsidiary supply of energy to the actively-moving land animals.

When bulk food, as contrasted with the particulate feeding of so many marine animals, even of earthworms, is to be consumed, jaws for mastication become a requisite for further evolution. The importance of the hinged jaw was an essential factor in the development of the vertebrates.

The genes control structure, and gene-changes influence the changes in structure. The environment sorts out the materials provided by the gene-changes, causing the extinction of some and the successful survival of others. And evolution is not just a passive process, but the phrase, random mutation acted upon by natural selection, is apt to give the impression that it is. To correct this impression, both random mutation and natural selection must be given a wide connotation. This can be best attained by a fuller appreciation of the role of the self-starting rhythms, whether continuous as in the plumose anemone, cyclic as in lugworms, seasonal as in normal reproduction, or erratic (or perhaps quasi-seasonal) as in the splitting of a starfish or an Amoeba into two. The continuous rhythm leads to appetitive behaviour, and appetitive behaviour set into more vigorous motion by external stimuli is an essential part of the biological drive. Over and above these, there are the faculties of selectivity, as in the feeding of Amoeba—or even the sea-anemone I foolishly fed to repletion—and choice, even in so lowly an organism as the larva of a marine bristle worm or of a barnacle. The analysis of these may in time reduce them all to a level of biochemical or biophysical reactions, but their synthesis produces something we are at a loss to explain or expound.

Perhaps we may summarise in this way. Nature produces the circumstances and the accidents (random mutation) and so she equips the animal with certain structures. In doing so she also equips it with the ability to make use of the available equipment as the need arises. The animal itself, by its adaptability, its power of selection (or choice) and by other such qualities, can exert an influence, however blind, on its own destiny. Or, to express it another way, an animal has more control of its future than has a pebble tossed about in the surf. This, as I see it, epitomises the philosophy I have referred to earlier as neo-vitalism. The older vitalists could not explain the mechanistic theories of animal behaviour for the reason that it was not possible to explain all living phenomena on mechanical (i.e. on biochemical and biophysical) grounds. The reply of the mechanists to this was that it was merely a matter of time before all the facts would be exposed. The vitalists' answer was to postulate some mystical quality in living matter; that after having reduced life to chemical and physical terms there yet remained some active vital principle—a sort of ultra-microscopic demon working the machine. The best we can say of these opposing camps is that the mechanist has a long way to go yet before his claim can be fully substantiated, and that until he has done so nobody can be absolutely certain that he is right. On the face of it the mechanist's claim is almost certain to be proved correct in the end, for each research into the ultimate springs of behaviour gives added confirmation. There is something else, however, which justifies a new vitalistic approach. It is not a mystical demon at the wheel, but the emergence of phenomena, based on chemical and physical laws, which, in their synthesis, give living matter its characteristic rhythms, drives and directiveness, the manifestations of which we describe as choice, initiative, adaptability, intelligence, and so on.

The main difficulty, as I see it, to holding the vitalistic view in biology lies in the elusiveness of its concepts and the inadequacy of our language to express them when they have taken shape. It may even be that the popularity of the mechanistic view is to some extent founded on the simplicity of its ideas and the ease with which it is expressed. Whether this is so or not, it gives rise, more especially in its extreme forms, to a warped perspective. For example, the extreme mechanist will deny that animals have a capacity for emotional behaviour, for intelligence, for personality, or for any of the qualities normally associated with human beings. At best he will grudgingly admit them for the higher apes, possibly for a few other of the more advanced mammals. Pressed to give a reason he will almost certainly reply that it is not possible to compare animal behaviour with that of humans.

It would be unwise to pursue this subject further within the compass of the few remaining pages. There is, however, one aspect of it that is usually overlooked. If the theory of organic evolution is correct, human beings have sprung from the same stock as the rest of the living world. In that case everything about us has its origins in the animal world and should be discernible in simpler form at lower levels of organisation. The distinctions are therefore quantitative and not qualitative. Or, to look at it from another angle, if all animal behaviour is reducible to chemical and physical reactions, so then is all human behaviour. To argue, as is often done by implication, that because the human brain possesses higher centres of nervous control we can draw a sharp line between the human and non-human, is to have one animated robot passing judgment on another animated robot and claiming to possess qualities the other has not. Certainly human evolution at the moment seems more the result of accident, or random chance, than that of any species studied by the biologist. If any species is groping its way blindly into the future it is ourselves, in spite of our claim to the exclusive possession of the faculty of reasoning and conceptual thought.

It is probable that the cynicism behind these last few remarks is more the result of looking at human evolution with too close a view. The far-distant future human may see our times, erratic and confused as they appear to us, as a rhythmic progression towards a well-defined goal. This future superman may, indeed, draw as between our behaviour and his a line as rigid as that we are apt to draw between our behaviour and that of the rest of the animal kingdom. He may see as much directiveness, and no more, as we see in the behaviour and evolution of animals. We, on the other hand, viewing present-day events at close range, minutely and continuously, see a chaos and an opportunism, a marching and counter-marching of events without visible control or direction, comparable in quality with what we in all likelihood should see in a gene-complex if our eyesight and insight were adequate to the occasion.

A lady, watching the coronation procession on a television screen, expressed herself as enthralled by the rhythm of marching troops. From the way she spoke it was clear that a number of soldiers walking along a street and not necessarily in step would have given her no pleasure. On the contrary, it would probably have caused her mental anguish, where troops in line and in step filled her with ecstacy. Ceremonial military manoeuvres, the beating of drums, music, poetry, dancing, even the waves beating on the shore have this strong appeal for us. And in each case the reason is the same. A sense of rhythm is deeply ingrained in us. It starts in our chromosomes, is heard in our heart-beat, manifests itself in our daily habits, is expressed in our architecture, indeed, in everything we make or do. It has "a mysterious power to please" and to dominate us.

Earlier I drew attention to the similarity between animal structures and human inventions as evidence that human activities represented a synthesis of the activities of the rest of the living world. Conversely, if the human appreciation of rhythm is also a synthesis of what obtains in the rest of the living world, then there is indicated a powerful factor in evolution. The tidal rhythm itself may not, in this connexion, be unworthy of further consideration.

It would be rash to assume that, if life began in the margins of the sea, the rhythm of the tides had become imparted to living matter. Yet, there is the coincidence; and certainly a rhythmic activity, in some form or other, is a fundamental property of living organisms. To recognise this may effect a desirable reconciliation of the opposing views of mechanists and vitalists. The one sees all living phenomena in strictly mechanical terms. The vitalist believes this insufficient in itself and postulates an unknown vital principle in addition. The inherent rhythmic activity is, of course, fundamentally mechanical, or physico-chemical. But being due to the synthesis of numerous interlocking mechanical reactions, its complete analysis has eluded us so far. It may yet prove to be the main ingredient of this long-sought vital principle.

INDEX